THE
Story
Tree

SISTER M. BERNARDA, C.PP.S., PH.D.
AND KATHERINE RANKIN

FAITH AND FREEDOM READERS

Ginn and Company

BOSTON NEW YORK CHICAGO
ATLANTA DALLAS PALO ALTO TORONTO

ACKNOWLEDGMENTS

Grateful acknowledgment is made to the following authors and publishers for permission to use and adapt copyrighted materials:

Abingdon Press for "The Three Horses," from *I Rode the Black Horse Far Away* by Ivy O. Eastwick, copyright © 1960 by Abingdon Press.

The Bruce Publishing Company, Milwaukee, for "Ludi, the Little St. Bernard," adapted from the book of the same title, by Norah Smaridge.

Child Life for the following stories from *Child Life* Magazine: "The Bumbershoot Wind" by Mary Calhoun, copyright 1956; "Mr. Zooly's Zoo" by Margaret Farquhar, copyright 1947; and "A Pet for St. Francis" by Irene Tamony, copyright 1958.

Thomas Y. Crowell Company for "A Real Cowboy," adapted from *Surprise for a Cowboy,* copyright 1950 by the author, Clyde Robert Bulla, and reprinted by permission of the publishers, Thomas Y. Crowell Company, New York.

Expression Company for "Easter Morning" by Louise Abney from *Choral Speaking Arrangements for the Junior High,* copyright © 1959, by Louise Abney, used by permission of Expression Company, Magnolia, Mass.

Faber and Faber Ltd. for "The Land of Ho-Ho-Hum," from *Laughing Time* by William Jay Smith, published by Faber and Faber Ltd.

Ginn and Company for the words and music for "St. Francis of Assisi," from *We Sing and Dance* by Sister Cecilia, S.C., Sister John Joseph, C.S.J., and Sister Rose Margaret, C.S.J.

J. B. Lippincott Company for "Music," from *Eleanor Farjeon's Poems for Children,* copyright © 1938 by Eleanor Farjeon, published by J. B. Lippincott Company.

Little, Brown & Company for "The Land of Ho-Ho-Hum," from *Laughing Time* by William Jay Smith, copyright 1955 by William Jay Smith, published by Little, Brown-Atlantic Monthly Press.

Lothrop, Lee and Shepard Co., Inc. for the selection from *Nino and His Fish* by Edith Thacher Hurd, copyright 1954 by Edith Thacher and Clement Hurd, adapted and reprinted by permission of Lothrop, Lee and Shepard, Inc.

The Macmillan Company for "The Seven White Cats," from *The Blue Teapot* by Alice Dalgliesh, copyright 1931 by The Macmillan Company, and used with their permission.

Harold Ober Associates for the following poems: "Candlemas Day,"

FAITH AND FREEDOM

NIHIL OBSTAT:

James J. Kortendick, M.A., S.T.B., CENSOR DEPUTATUS

IMPRIMATUR:

† Patrick A. O'Boyle, D.D., ARCHBISHOP OF WASHINGTON
Washington, January 15, 1964

COMMISSION ON AMERICAN CITIZENSHIP

THE CATHOLIC UNIVERSITY OF AMERICA

Rt. Rev. Msgr. William J. McDonald, *President of the Commission*

Rt. Rev. Msgr. Joseph A. Gorham, *Director*

Sister Mary Lenore, O.P., *Curriculum Consultant*

The Story Tree

The story tree! The story tree!
From topmost branches you can see
Birds and beasts and honeybees,
Elephants who're hard to please,
Bronchos, burros, buffaloes,
Cats, and dogs, and cawing crows!

You'll wish you were the boy who flew
His "bumbershoot" into the blue;
You'll wish your days were spent in camp,
(But sometimes camps are very damp;)
And what's a book without some tales
Of Indians and cowboy trails?

We hope that when you hear the bells
That Carla heard, then you can tell
That, when she prayed for needed care,
The Blessed Mother heard her prayer!

How could you climb the story tree?
Just turn a page and you will see
That, from the tree, you'll glimpse a view
Of boys and girls who could be you!

Contents

Once Upon a Time Tales

Under Western Skies

Golden Days

All stories not otherwise credited have been written especially for this book by Katherine Rankin.

Can It Be True?

The Land of Ho-Ho-Hum

When you want to go wherever you please,
Just sit down in an old valise,
   And fasten the strap
   Around your lap,
And fly off over the apple trees.

And fly for days and days and days
Over rivers, brooks, and bays
   Until you come
   To the Ho-Ho-Hum
Where the Lion roars, and the Donkey brays.

Where the Unicorn's tied to a golden chain,
And Umbrella Flowers drink the rain.
   After that,
   Put on your hat,
And sit down and fly home again.

WILLIAM JAY SMITH

9

The Bumbershoot Wind

It was a wild March day. *Whoooo*, went the wind around the corner of the house. It tossed the long fingers of the treetops and ruffled the spring flowers in the garden.

Hector watched from the window. "Where does the wind go?" he wondered. He decided to find out.

The first thing to do was to find an umbrella. Hector hunted through all the umbrellas in the umbrella stand in the front hall.

Would Mother's little green umbrella do? No. Would Daddy's long thin umbrella do? No. How about Grandfather's big black umbrella with the wooden squirrel head on the handle? Grandfather called the old umbrella his *bumbershoot*.

Yes! Surely a bumbershoot would do.

Hector picked it up and ran out on the high front porch. He opened the bumbershoot and smiled. The umbrella's cloth was heavy, and it would be easy to hold onto the squirrel head. Grandfather's bumbershoot was just right for flying!

Hector waited until the wind whistled by. Then. holding the umbrella high, Hector stepped off the porch. *Whuff!* The wind caught up the old bumbershoot, and away sailed Hector.

First the wind whisked him to the backyard where his mother was hanging out clothes.

When she saw Hector she called, "Hector! Come down this minute."

Hector laughed and called, "I'm sorry. I can't. I'm going to see where the wind goes. I'll be back when the wind changes."

Then the wind and the bumbershoot and Hector sailed away over the treetops. Hector's mother ran into the house and telephoned the weatherman.

"Quick!" she cried. "When will the wind change? Please make the wind change right away!"

The weatherman said the wind wasn't supposed to change for several days. He was very sorry, but there was nothing he could do about it.

In the meantime the wind had carried Hector over the highest church in town and twice around the town clock.

In the town below, men and women pointed and shouted, "Help! A run-away umbrella!"

And the boys and the girls looked up and sighed and wished *they* had bumbershoots. They knew, of course, that just any old umbrella wouldn't do.

Some ducks, who were trying to fly north, got caught in the wind and flew along beside Hector for a while.

Then the wind popped down to help push a sail-boat on a lake, and the ducks flew north again, quacking good-by to Hector.

Little bits of water flew in Hector's face, and his toes skipped along the waves by the sailboat. The man in the sailboat saw him and called, "Good sailing today, isn't it?"

Before Hector really got wet, the wind whisked the bumbershoot high in the air again. As they sailed over a hilltop, Hector saw some children flying kites.

"Hi!" he shouted. "This is better than kites."

He started to tell them where the wind goes, but just then a large red kite sailed up behind him. The kite's long ribboned tail twisted around the bumbershoot's handle.

On the ground a boy was pulling the kite, and Hector began to drop down out of the wind. Just in time, he pulled the kite tail away from the handle and sailed on.

14

Then a R-R-R-M-M-M-M, louder than the roar of the wind, sounded in the sky. An airplane was coming straight at Hector!

He bobbed the bumbershoot's handle up and down and kicked his legs, trying to get out of the way, but the airplane pilot had seen him. Quickly the pilot turned the plane away and missed Hector.

A woman, looking out of the airplane window, saw Hector and his bumbershoot and screamed, "A space ship! Help!"

"Man from Mars!" shouted a man.

"No, it's a bird," cried another man in the airplane.

Hector just laughed and bobbed his bumbershoot as he flew out of sight.

Now the wind carried Hector high over valleys, and high over great seas. Sometimes the bumbershoot ducked down near the ground, and boys and girls in strange clothes threw balls and toys up to Hector. He couldn't let go of his umbrella to catch them, and so he just waved his feet.

"Hi!" he shouted, "I'm going where the wind goes."

16

Sometimes, surprised birds flew up to take a look at Hector. One even tried to peck at him, but Hector bobbed the bumbershoot and shouted, "Go away!" The bird flew away.

Swish! The wind went down low and threw dust into a lion's eye and blew an elephant's ears inside out. Hector swished down, too, so close that the lion snapped at him.

Again the wind roared high over more seas and mountains and rivers. It was getting toward suppertime, and Hector saw his own town below.

Then the wind changed. It changed from a wild, roaring wind to a soft, gentle breeze. Then, easy as a feather, the breeze set Hector down in front of his house.

"I'm back, Mother," he called at the top of his voice. "The wind changed."

"Oh, thank goodness," Mother said, hugging him.

"I found out where the wind goes," Hector told her. "It goes all around the world and back again."

Hector patted the squirrel-head handle of his grandfather's umbrella. Then he put it away until the next time a bumbershoot wind came along.

MARY CALHOUN

Azor and the Turtle

Azor Makes a New Friend

Azor Peach could play ball pretty well. He could swim pretty well. He could do a lot of things very well.

But there was one strange thing about Azor Peach. Animals talked to him. They *really* did. It was no "pussy-horsie-doggie" talk either. The things they told him were *important* things.

It wasn't Azor who thought there was anything strange about it. It was other people. Grownups laughed at him and scolded him. Big boys laughed at him and called him a baby. And, of course, nobody believed him.

Early one morning Azor saw his brother Matthew, and Chrissie's brother Jimmer, starting down toward Orne Street. He knew right away where they were going because they were carrying nets on long poles.

Matthew and Jimmer were going to the pond to catch turtles to sell for twenty-five cents apiece to the children in town.

Azor had always wanted to go along with them. If he could catch even one turtle himself, he would have twenty-five whole cents. Then he could go down to the store and for once in his life eat *enough* potato chips. But Matthew had always said he was too little—that he would only talk and frighten the turtles away.

So he was very much surprised when his brother called to him, "Hey, Azor! You can come along this time, if you want to, because we need someone to watch the box so the turtles won't get away. We're going to stay all day and catch thousands! But remember now—no talking! Hear?"

Azor would much rather have brought a net and tried to catch some turtles himself, but it was better to go along and not catch any, than not to go at all. So he ran back into the kitchen and got a piece of chocolate cake and a bottle of root beer from the icebox. Then he raced after Matthew and Jimmer and caught up with them at the foot of Gingerbread Lane.

When they got to the pond, they dug a hole at the edge of the water. They put their bottles of root beer in it to keep cool. Matthew and Jimmer pulled a big box from behind an old red house and put it in the grass under a tree.

They left Azor with the lunches beside the box and told him not to make a sound. Then they went down to the edge of the water with their nets. They threw some bread crumbs into the water and waited for the turtles to come.

While Azor sat and watched them he thought of what his father had told him about the pond. He said there was an old story that the bottom of the pond was paved with pennies!

20

Pretty soon Matthew and Jimmer began to bring turtles and put them into the box. By lunchtime they had seven. While they all drank their root beer and ate their cake, Azor listened to them talking.

"Jingoes!" said Matthew. "Do you know how much money that is? That's one dollar and seventy-five cents! That's how much! And we have the whole afternoon to go!"

"If we get seven more turtles this afternoon," Jimmer said, "it will be more than the other boys ever got in one day!"

"It won't be, if you stay here all afternoon talking," said Azor.

So they went down to the water again. After a while they brought two more turtles, and then there was a long time when they didn't bring any. Azor lay in the grass, looking into the box.

There was a big turtle in there and two middle-sized ones, but the rest were tiny ones, born that very spring. Some of them had their heads and paws drawn into their shells, and their pointed little tails were wrapped across their bottoms. The others crawled around and looked up at Azor as if they weren't afraid, or even surprised, that they had been caught.

Azor wondered what it was like to be a turtle, and the very second he was wondering that, the biggest turtle blinked his eyes slowly and looked up at him.

"I'll make it worth your while if you tip the box," said the turtle. "Come back at the same time, same place, tomorrow."

So Azor turned over the box and watched the turtles crawl over the grass and plop back into the pond. He was glad the littlest ones were going back to their mothers.

But when the last one had slid down into the water, Azor suddenly thought of Matthew and Jimmer down by the pond. He started to feel quite queer. He thought it must be time to go home. So he did.

22

The Turtle Keeps His Promise

Azor got tired very fast that night, because every place he went in the house Matthew seemed to be there ahead of him with his jaw stuck 'way out and shaking his fist.

At last his mother said, "What's the matter with you boys tonight?"

So Azor told her, and that made Matthew even madder than he was before. The second Azor saw his brother starting to get madder, he remembered that his mother didn't like Matthew to sell turtles. But by then he was in the middle of the story and he had to finish it. The only thing he didn't tell was why he tipped over the box.

After that he went up to bed.

The next day he only had time to get to the pond and sit down under the tree when the big turtle came crawling up out of the water.

He had something in his mouth that looked like an old penny, only much bigger—almost as big as a half dollar. He dropped it in the grass in front of Azor. It was all wet and gunky, but Azor picked it up anyway and put it in his pocket.

"Thank you very much," he said.

Then the turtle went away, and Azor went back home.

After supper Azor was in the kitchen, shining the penny so that it would look better and not smell so badly. His father came in and watched Azor for a minute. Then he asked him where the penny came from.

Azor opened his mouth to say, "The turtle gave it to me for tipping the box," but he caught himself just in time. "I got it up by the pond," he said.

His father picked up the penny and looked at it.

"Hmmm!" he said. "I'm going to take this over to Lot Snow and see what he thinks. I'll be right back."

And he was gone. Mr. Snow was the man who last year gave twenty-five cents to everyone who brought him an Indian-head penny.

Azor was getting ready for bed when his father came back and called him in a loud voice—not an angry-loud voice but in a pleased-loud voice.

"Azor! Come on down here!"

24

When he got downstairs, everybody was in the living room. Matthew's mouth was quite wide open, but he wasn't saying anything. He was just staring at two piles of money on the table.

"Well, Azor," his father said. "You're a rich man. That old penny of yours was a 1793 cent—one of the first coins ever made in this country. Lot Snow bought it for *fifty dollars!* Pick it up, son, it's all yours."

Azor picked it up. Except for potato-chip money, it went into the bank with the money Azor was saving for a sailboat when he got to be twelve.

MAUDE CROWLEY

Questions

I visited the animals
That live in our zoo;
And there are lots of questions
I've saved for you.

Why is the zebra's skin so tight?
The hippo's skin so loose?
Why does the old owl look so wise?
The peacock such a goose?

What do the monkeys talk about
In their excited way?
I'm sure it would be lots of fun
If we knew what they say!

The turtle's house is fastened on
As tight as tight can be!
Are little boys as queer to them
As turtles are to me?

RUTH COLLAT

Mr. Zooly's Zoo

Mr. Zooly kept a very fine zoo.   He had monkeys and lions and bears and elephants.

Every day Mr. Zooly kept getting more animals until, finally, he didn't have room for any more.

Everybody liked the animals except Mr. Crabtree. He lived all by himself in a great big house next door to the zoo.   The noise of the animals bothered Mr. Crabtree.

Mr. Zooly tried to keep the animals quiet, but he couldn't.   The lions roared, the bears growled, and the monkeys screamed.

One day Mr. Crabtree came to call on Mr. Zooly.

"Mr. Zooly," he said, "please keep your animals quiet. If you don't, I will have to report you to the police. It is against the *law* to disturb the peace, and your animals are disturbing *my* peace. If I report you, the Chief of Police will make you send all the animals back to the countries they came from."

Then Mr. Crabtree shook his cane very hard at Mr. Zooly and went back to his great big house.

After that poor Mr. Zooly tried all the harder to keep his animals quiet. He fed the animals all kinds of wonderful food, and he fed them lots and lots of it. But the animals were very, very noisy.

Then something happened! A friend of Mr. Zooly's sent him three big elephants, and there just wasn't any more room in the zoo.

28

"We will have to find room for the new elephants," said Mr. Zooly. "It would be very rude to send them back. Perhaps we could squeeze the lions into a smaller cage and put the new elephants in the old lion cage."

Now, this meant moving the bears out of their cages to make room for the lions. This meant moving the monkeys out of their cages to make room for the bears. Every animal in the zoo had to be moved to make room for another.

The animals didn't like the idea of moving into smaller cages. So, when Mr. Zooly moved them, they made more noise than ever before.

"Grr! Eeeeek, eeeeek! Bark, bark!" said the animals, as they moved from one cage to another.

Mr. Crabtree was madder than ever. He ran out of his great big house into the street.

"Come at once," he said to a policeman standing on a street corner. "Mr. Zooly's animals are making so much noise that I can't eat or sleep or even hear myself think. You must send them all away."

The policeman blew his whistle. Soon a great many policemen and the Chief of Police and Mr. Crabtree were standing at the gate of Mr. Zooly's zoo. The Chief of Police rang the bell.

The noise was terrible. The lions were roaring,
the monkeys were screaming, and the bears were
growling.

When Mr. Zooly came to the gate, the Chief of
Police said, "You must stop this noise at once. Your
animals are disturbing the peace."

"Oh, dear," said Mr. Zooly. "I certainly do not
want to disturb the peace, and I do want my animals
to be happy. But I don't know what to do."

Then he told the Chief of Police about the new elephants.

"Well," said the Chief of Police, "I'm very fond of elephants, myself, but you must keep your animals quiet. I'll give you until tomorrow morning. If you cannot do it by then, the animals must be sent away."

All night long Mr. Zooly worried about his animals. Then, early the next morning, he had an idea. He went to call on Mr. Crabtree.

"Mr. Crabtree," said Mr. Zooly, "why do you live next door to my zoo if the noise bothers you so much?"

"I would rather live anywhere else in the world," said Mr. Crabtree, "but no one will buy my house. It's much too big."

"I will buy your house," said Mr. Zooly. "It will not be too big for my elephants. It will make the best elephant house in the world."

So Mr. Zooly bought the house from Mr. Crabtree that very day. And that night Mr. Crabtree moved to the other side of town.

Mr. Crabtree's house became a fine elephant house. The elephants were very happy in it. The other animals were happy, too, now that they were moved back to their own cages.

31

But that isn't the end of the story. Oh, no. After a while Mr. Crabtree began to miss the animals. So, every now and then, he visited Mr. Zooly and his animals. Mr. Crabtree liked to visit the elephants most of all because they were living in his old house.

Aren't people funny sometimes?

MARGARET FARQUHAR

32

The Taxicab That Went Mad

There was once a farmer who lived in the country about fifty miles away from a big city. He had a wife and several children, and his old mother lived with them, too.

She was a very wise old woman, for she had lived a long, long time. When you grow old, you grow wise.

One day the farmer went to the city, and when he was there, he bought—now what do you think?

You'd never guess. He bought an old taxicab. He happened to hear of one that was going cheap, and when he saw it he felt that he would like to have it.

"It's getting a bit hard for granny to go about and visit the neighbors," he thought. "And it will come in useful for lots of things. It has been a good year, and I can easily spend thirty dollars," for that was what the cab cost.

So he bought the cab and drove it home.

Now, this taxicab had never been outside the city in its life. Not really right out into the country. It had seen pictures of the country. It had heard people talk about the country, but it had never been nearer than the edge of the big city.

The taxi got more and more excited as the farmer drove it along the roads. It was springtime, and everything was looking most beautiful.

The taxi had never before seen so much blue sky or so many trees. It hadn't known there were so many trees in the world. Cows and sheep, too, and a fat old pig with a lot of real little pink pigs. It was wonderful!

At last they came to the village where the farmer lived. He drove through the big gate into the farm-yard.

The farmer stopped the taxicab in front of the house and blew its horn. Toot! Toot! Toot! The farmer's wife and children and the old granny all came running out to see who was arriving in a taxicab.

"The idea of coming all the way home in a taxicab!" said the farmer's wife. "What ever in the world made you do that?"

"I've bought it," said the farmer, as he got out of the cab. "It's going to stay here on the farm."

35

Now, the taxicab had not realized that it was to stay in the country. When it heard this news, it became so excited at the thought of always living among the trees and the chickens and the cows that it suddenly went mad. It started running around the yard at top speed. It went on and on, faster and faster, round and round and round.

The farmer tried to jump on, but he fell off and was almost run over. The farmer's wife called, "Stop! stop!" The children screamed. Nobody could do anything to stop the cab.

Clatter, clatter, bang, bang, rattle, rattle! The cab seemed to be running a race—a race with nobody.

Everyone stood staring, not knowing what to do. Everyone but granny. She ran into the house as fast as her old legs would carry her.

In the kitchen she took her big red apron from its hook by the door. She leaned out of the window, and just as the taxi was about to pass she waved the red apron in front of it.

The taxi stopped dead. It just *could* not pass the red signal. Of course, when it stopped, it soon cooled down. Then it realized how very foolishly it had been acting.

It never again went mad, but spent the rest of its life very happily in the country. You'd be surprised how many miles that old taxi ran and how useful it was.

But wasn't it clever of the old granny to think of her red apron? I should never have thought of that, should you?

ROSE FYLEMAN

Animal Friends
Far and Near

Feather or Fur

When you watch for
Feather or fur
Feather or fur
Do not stir
Do not stir.

Feather or fur
Come crawling
Creeping
Some come peeping
Some by night
And some by day.
Most come gently,
All come softly,
Do not scare
A friend away.

When you watch for
Feather or fur
Feather or fur
Do not stir
Do not stir.

JOHN BECKER

Ludi, the Little St. Bernard

Ludi Runs Away

Ludi was a little St. Bernard puppy. He lived in the St. Bernard Lodge, high up in the mountains. No one else lived there but the monks and their dogs, so it was sometimes lonely for a playful little puppy.

St. Bernard puppies grow up to be big, strong dogs. They are trained to help the monks save travelers who are lost in the snow in the mountains. Ludi was still a puppy. He had not yet been trained, but he had watched some of the bigger dogs learning how to help travelers.

One day, when Ludi was playing in the big pen where the dogs were kept, he saw something! The gate in the fence was open a tiny bit! Brother Joseph must have forgotten to close it when he came to feed the puppies.

40

Ludi crept nearer. He looked to see if anyone was watching him. Then Ludi squeezed his fat little body through the opening in the fence and trotted to the edge of the mountain road.

Ludi looked along the rough road that went down to the valley. No one was in sight. He looked the other way. The road seemed to disappear in the clouds. There was nothing up there except great mountains, covered with ice and snow.

So Ludi decided to trot down to the road that led to the village. He was sure he would find a boy to be his master in the village.

He had not gone far when he heard a noise. It was a puffing, panting kind of noise. Ludi stood still. What was that? Then he remembered. It was the noise a car makes when the motor won't start.

Quickly Ludi ran and peeped around a tree. It was the monks' car. Brother Peter was sitting in the jeep, and Brother Francis was standing beside it.

"I shall pray that you get back safely," said Brother Francis. "This jeep sounds as if it's ready to fall to pieces."

Brother Peter laughed. "There's plenty of life in it yet." Suddenly he shook his head. "Oh, I've forgotten the rosary beads for the schoolteacher's son."

The two monks started back to the Lodge. As soon as their backs were turned, Ludi jumped into the jeep and hid under an old blanket. Brother Peter soon came back, and the jeep started with a jerk. Ludi bumped his nose. He hurt his paws, trying to dig them into the floor as the jeep rattled and banged down the rough road.

When the jeep stopped, Ludi waited until Brother Peter got out. Then he crawled from under the blanket and looked around. The jeep was still on the mountain, but they were a long way from the Lodge.

Ludi watched Brother Peter cross to a shrine by the road. It was a wooden shrine with a statue of Our Lady in it. Her blue gown was faded, but she smiled sweetly. Brother Peter knelt to pray his rosary.

Suddenly Ludi heard someone whistling. He looked down the side of the mountain and saw a boy, climbing a steep path.

Ludi jumped out of the jeep and scampered across the road. How could he get down to the path where the little boy was? Ludi ran down this path and that. He stopped and looked again. Now the whistling sounded far away. He could not see the boy anywhere, and the jeep was gone.

Lost

Ludi trotted on for some time. At last he came to a tree where he rested and looked for something to eat. He was getting hungry. He sniffed around, but he could find nothing to eat. Close by, he found a little stream where he could get a drink.

Then Ludi felt something soft touch his nose, cold and wet. It was starting to snow.

The snow was falling faster as Ludi began to trot up the path. He whined softly. He must find a place where he could sleep and forget how hungry he was.

As he went up and up the mountain road, Ludi saw the shrine where Brother Peter had stopped to pray. His tail lifted, and he began to trot faster. He would curl up at the foot of the shrine. When Ludi came nearer to the shrine, he saw a boy on the ground. It was the same boy Ludi had tried to follow hours ago.

Ludi ran up and barked, but the boy did not move. Ludi barked louder, and the boy opened his eyes.

"A puppy!" he cried. "Where's your master?"

The boy moved a little and made a moaning sound. Ludi had never heard a sound like this before, but he knew that this boy needed help.

44

When a St. Bernard dog finds a man in the snow, he first licks his face to waken him—because the man would freeze to death if he slept in the snow. Somehow or other, perhaps because he had watched the monks train some of the bigger dogs, Ludi seemed to know what to do.

He began to lick the boy's face. He licked and licked. He gave the boy's ear a gentle nip. The boy opened his eyes again.

"Are you still here, pup?" he said. He looked up at the statue of Our Lady. "Holy Mary, please send this dog's master," he whispered. "My leg hurts, and my head hurts—and I'm terribly cold."

Ludi seemed to know that a St. Bernard dog stands over the man he is saving, and warms him with his own body. Ludi was not big, but he did the very best he could. He crept to the boy and curled up close beside him.

"That feels good," the boy said, trying to smile. Then he slid his hand into his pocket. "Here, pup. This is all I have."

It was a bit of cold meat. Ludi ate it and began to feel sleepy. His eyes were half closed when suddenly he heard a puffing, whining, panting noise.

Ludi knew that sound. It was the sound a car makes when it is trying to climb the mountain road.

Ludi ran quickly to the middle of the road. As the car came into sight Ludi barked his loudest. He barked and jumped in the middle of the road.

It was the monks' jeep! It slowed down—just in time.

"Ludi!" Brother Peter jumped out. "How did you get here?"

Ludi was running about, barking fiercely. He ran to the boy and back. He jumped at Brother Peter and ran again to the boy. Brother Peter knew what the pup was trying to say. He followed him quickly and knelt by the boy. He touched him gently, and the boy opened his eyes.

"Thank God," he said. "I'm half frozen and—I'm lost!"

46

"Don't try to talk now," Brother Peter said. He carried the boy to the jeep. "I'll take you to the Lodge," he said. "Ludi, you sit with him."

Ludi curled up near the boy, and the boy patted him. Before long, both Ludi and the boy were sleeping.

The next thing Ludi knew, two monks were carrying the boy into the Lodge. Brother Peter and Brother Francis were smiling at Ludi.

"I was going to let Ludi start training tomorrow with the big dogs," Brother Peter said, "but he has saved his first person all on his own!"

"He must be hungry," Brother Francis said. "I'll get him some supper."

Brother Peter carried Ludi into the kitchen. A great fire burned in the fireplace, and there was the good smell of beef soup.

Brother Francis brought him a large dish of soup. More monks came into the kitchen. They smiled at Ludi and petted him and talked about him.

"Ludi will turn out to be one of the best dogs we have ever had," Brother Francis said. "Just wait and see!"

Ludi wagged his tail happily and went to sleep.

NORAH SMARIDGE

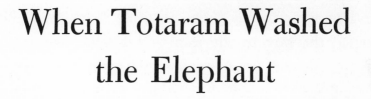

When Totaram Washed
the Elephant

Totaram was lying on his back under a tree, watching the crows play King on the Mountain. They played on the tall flagpole which stood in the village.

One crow would fly to the top of it and perch on the tip. Then the others would tease him with loud voices and fly down upon him, trying to knock him off.

The pole was smooth, and no crow could stay king for long. But what fun he had during that time! He would flap his wings and tell them all what a fine crow he was, and then—! Down would come another crow on top of him and send him flapping into the air.

As Totaram lay watching this game he suddenly heard a sound behind him. He jumped as a sleeping dog does before a cart wheel touches it.

"Have you nothing better to do than watch the crows?" asked the man beside him.

Totaram made a deep bow, because the man was
the keeper of the elephants and an important person.

"What is your mother doing?" asked the man.

"She is working in the fields," said Totaram.

"And your father?"

"He has gone to the jungle to cut bushes to put
around his fields to keep out the wild pigs."

"And your sister?"

"She is making something for our supper," said
Totaram, who did not feel very comfortable.

"And you?"

"I am doing nothing at all," said Totaram slowly.
"But truly I would do something if I could find it to
do."

"Why are you not with the other boys watching the cows?"

Totaram hung his head. "Because, O Great One," he said, "I teased one of the cows with my pointed stick. And she ran into the village and upset four jars of milk as she ran. How could I know that she would mind the stick so much? And the milkman beat me and sent me away."

"Little Trouble Maker," said the man, "I will give you another chance, but there must not be any more foolishness or teasing. You must not act like one of the monkeys in the jungle."

Totaram lifted his head.

"I want a boy to wash the big elephant," the keeper went on. "Every Wednesday and every Saturday I will take her to the pool near the gate of the city. You must meet me there when the sun is in the middle of the sky. Bring with you some coconut shells to scrub with."

Totaram could hardly believe his good luck and ran off to tell the boys about it. The keeper of the elephants looked at the crow on top of the pole, and then he looked at the boys who were waving their arms about and talking.

"They are much alike, boys and crows," the keeper said smiling, and went away.

Totaram thought that Wednesday would never come. He teased the gray kitten, pulling its tail until it mewed and his sister cried.

His mother sighed and said, "Little Trouble Maker, use your strong arms at this," and gave him the heavy stick to pound the brown rice.

At last Wednesday came. When the sun was high, Totaram started for the pool. He arrived before the elephant and sat down under a tree to wait.

Then came the elephant, like a black mountain, toward him. Totaram felt the size of a rabbit, and then he felt the size of a mouse. Then he thought, "If it comes much nearer, I shall be as nothing at all!"

51

The keeper laughed at him. "Are you a squirrel come to wash my elephant?" he asked. "You looked larger in your village. I could use twenty of you little ones."

Totaram's knees shook as the dry grass does in the strong winds of the hot season.

But Totaram held on to his coconut shells and followed the keeper down to the water. There the big elephant gave a sigh of happiness and lay down on her side. Totaram climbed on top of her and began to scrub her with his coconut shells.

It was long, hard work. "Surely I am cleaning a mile of elephant," he said to himself. He looked to see if the keeper would say that his work was finished, but the man was smoking a water pipe under the tree.

By now Totaram had forgotten to be afraid, and he was even brave enough to scrub in the elephant's big ears and around her little eyes.

That evening, when Totaram went home, he had money in his pocket. He was so proud that he called all his friends together to tell them what a wonderful boy he was. And he pulled the gray kitten's tail again.

When Saturday came, Totaram's sister and two village boys followed him into the city and to the pool. The keeper lay down and went to sleep under the tree. Totaram began scrubbing behind the elephant's ears as if he had been cleaning elephant's ears all his life.

"O my grandfathers!" said one boy. "Her right ear is as large as my father's dinner plate."

"Her left ear is the size of my uncle's umbrella," said the other boy. "Aren't you afraid, Totaram?"

"Oh my, no," said Totaram. "The elephant may be very large, with ears like umbrellas, but she is as stupid as a mountain." He began to jump up and down on her back to show them how brave he was.

The elephant moved one ear slowly, like a banana leaf in the wind. Totaram went on jumping. The elephant moved the other ear slowly, like a sail in a fishing boat. Totaram went on jumping.

Suddenly the elephant reached up her trunk, picked up Totaram, and ducked him in the muddy water. Then she lifted him up and shook him the way a cat shakes a mouse. Then she ducked him again. The two boys and Totaram's sister laughed until they fell down and rolled over and over.

"The elephant is as stupid as a mountain, is she?" called one boy.

"Now you know how my gray kitten feels when you pull its tail," said Totaram's sister.

"O queen of elephants," cried Totaram, "set me down, and I'll never pull the gray kitten's tail again."

The elephant shook him again.

"O wisest of elephants," said Totaram, "truly I will never jump on you again."

Then the elephant set him down, and Totaram ran away into the jungle near the village. There he could not see the other children, who were still laughing.

Late that afternoon his mother found him, sleeping with his head on a gray root. He was saying something, and when she leaned over him she heard Totaram say, "Truly, I will never pull the gray kitten's tail again."

IRENE MOTT BOSE

The Three Horses

Three horses came
to the meadow's edge—
they poked their noses
over the hedge.

One was gray,
one was white,
and one was black
as a winter's night.

I patted the white horse,
I stroked the gray,
and I rode the black horse
far away.

We went by the wood,
we went by the hill,
we galloped along
by Medlicott Mill.

Oh! if my mother
should question you—
I may be back
in an hour or two.

IVY O. EASTWICK

56

The Seven White Cats

The Terrible Day

The seven white cats lived on the Saunders' farm. No one believed in the seven white cats until he had seen them. "Seven white cats? Nonsense!" That was what everyone said.

But there were the cats, plainly to be seen if one took the trouble to walk up the hill to the farmhouse. Often Miranda, the farmer's little girl, would be sitting on the steps with all the cats around her.

It was Miranda who had given them their names. The mother of them all was Blue Eyes. The two half-grown kittens were the Angel Cat and the Odd Cat. The Angel Cat was a beautiful white, with large blue eyes like her mother's. The Odd Cat was a bit queer looking, and his eyes did not match, for one was blue and one was yellow-brown.

Then there were the four smallest kittens. They were little balls of white fur, always playing with each other in the grass or chasing each other's tails.

57

Three of them were Tim, Tip, and Tinker. The fourth was called Stub, because he had only a stub of a tail. The kittens had been brought up in the barn and, sad to tell, Stub's tail had been stepped on by the ox!

Miranda was very fond of cats. Her father, Mr. Saunders, was not at all fond of cats, but he was fond of Miranda and so he allowed her to keep them. At least, he allowed her to keep them until one terrible day when everything went wrong.

The trouble began the first thing in the morning, when Mr. Saunders went to milk the cows. Stub was in the barn as usual. He ran right in front of Mr. Saunders, who tripped over him and dropped the milk pail. This made Mr. Saunders very angry.

Things kept on happening all through the day. When Mrs. Saunders went into the dairy, she found Blue Eyes helping herself to the biggest pan of cream.

A little later in the day Tinker climbed up the curtains in the living room and tore a large hole in one of them. Tip tangled himself up in Mrs. Saunders' knitting, and Tim pulled things out of her workbasket.

"Cats are more trouble than they are worth!" said Mrs. Saunders.

"There are not going to be any cats on this farm," said Mr. Saunders.

"Oh, please, Papa!" said Miranda.

Mr. Saunders did not even listen to Miranda. When he made up his mind to be firm, he was very firm.

That afternoon, when Miranda was out visiting one of her friends, he put all seven cats into a large box, loaded the box on the oxcart along with baskets of vegetables, and started off.

First of all, he drove up the hill. At the first house he left Stub, because the children there liked Stub's funny short tail.

At the next house he left Angel Cat.

Then he drove on. He came to a neat house with a long patch of yellow flowers growing outside the gate. Without stopping, he dropped Tinker among the flowers.

A little way along the road there was a big farm-house. A blue wooden cradle stood under the maple tree at the gate, and the farmer's little boy was helping his mother put the baby into it.

"Such a nice family should have a cat," said Mr. Saunders. He held Tim up so they could see him.

"We'd like to have a white kitten," said the farmer's rosy-cheeked wife.

As he drove along the road Mr. Saunders whistled cheerfully, for now there were only three more cats. Soon he came to a cottage with a bright red roof.

"A house with a bright red roof always looks better if there is a white cat somewhere around," he said. He left Tip.

In a cottage by the sea lived a very old lady. She was sitting by the open window as Mr. Saunders drove up and dropped Blue Eyes into her lap.

"Here's fine company for you on long winter evenings," he said.

There was only one cat left, the Odd Cat. Mr. Saunders was not at all sure that anyone would care to have a cat with such strange eyes. Then he found an old fisherman who liked the Odd Cat very much.

"Cats with eyes like that are lucky," said the fisherman.

Mr. Saunders sang happily as he drove toward home.

When the oxcart stopped in front of his own farmhouse, Mr. Saunders saw Miranda sitting on the steps. Big tears were running down her cheeks, and she gave her father a sad look. Mr. Saunders did not say anything. He drove into the barn.

Miranda kept on crying. It seemed as if nothing in the world would stop her tears. She was still crying when she went to bed, yet she said nothing at all.

"This is more than I can stand," said Mr. Saunders. "We must do something to make her forget those cats."

Mrs. Saunders shook her head sadly.

A Visit to the Lighthouse

The next morning Mr. Saunders told Miranda that he would take her for a ride to the lighthouse. Miranda had always wanted to go to the lighthouse, but she did not even smile.

"Yes, Papa," was all she said, in a sad little voice.

They rode together for miles and came to the lighthouse. It was very white and neat, the rocks were black, and the sea and sky were blue.

As they went up the path to the lighthouse a baby came out of the door. She laughed and held out her hands to Miranda. Miranda smiled—just a little smile. The baby's mother came out to see that the baby was safe.

And then—a black and white cat came through the doorway. Behind her came four kittens: a black and white kitten, a black kitten, a gray kitten, and—last of all—a white kitten with blue eyes.

Miranda sat right down on the rocky ground and called to the kitten. She picked it up and hugged it to her. For the first time that day she looked happy.

"Your little girl seems to be very fond of cats," said the lighthouse keeper's wife.

"She certainly is," answered Mr. Saunders, but he did not look very pleased.

Miranda sat and held the white kitten.

"Would you like to take my white kitten home with you?" asked the lighthouse keeper's wife.

"Yes! Oh, yes, I would!" answered Miranda. "May I, Papa?"

"I suppose so," sighed her father. "Now let's go and see the light."

Miranda would not let go of the white kitten even for a moment. She was much more interested in the kitten than she was in the lighthouse. She wanted to start for home right away.

As they came up the road to the farmhouse, Miranda and Mr. Saunders could hardly believe their eyes. There, sitting quietly on the doorstep, were Blue Eyes, the Odd Cat, and the Angel Cat.

The four kittens, Tim, Tip, Tinker, and Stub, scampered around in the grass.

64

"Why, here are all the cats! They must have walked home." Miranda gathered all the cats she could hold in her arms and hugged them. "I'm so happy," she said.

Mr. Saunders said nothing at all, but after that there were eight cats at the farmhouse. And all around the countryside people said to each other, "Have you seen a white cat anywhere? We had one here the other day!"

ALICE DALGLIESH

A Pet for St. Francis

Juan patted his burro as they stood in front of the church, waiting their turn to receive the blessing of St. Francis. This was the day on which all the pets in the village were brought to the church in honor of that gentle saint who made all birds and animals his brothers.

Juan was sure that Chico was the finest burro in all Mexico. Surely he would have the largest blessing of all—larger than the tiny dog next to him. Certainly he was larger than the red and green parrot which screamed in his ear on the other side.

Juan pushed the red rose in behind Chico's ear. "Pedro the goat, and my fat pink pig at home are not as fine as you, my brave Chico." Juan put his face against the burro's neck.

"Hee-haw, hee-haw," cried Chico, shaking his long ears.

Out from the red rose behind his ear flew a yellow bee. It went straight to Chico's wet black nose and stung him.

"Heeeeeeeee-haaaaaaaa!" Chico kicked up his heels and galloped past the pool by the village fountain.

Juan threw up his hands, then walked home as slowly as a turtle. He would have to take Pedro to the church after all. A goat would not get half as big a blessing as Chico would have had!

Behind the fence of Juan's yard, Pedro was eating some straw, the food he liked best of all. "Maaa!"

"What a lot of cleaning you will take!" Juan took a brush and went to work on Pedro.

With a shining Pedro close to his heels, Juan again walked to the church.

"Mind your manners, Pedro," Juan told him. "No pushing, no biting. Understand?"

Pedro jerked his head up and down.

When Juan and Pedro reached the church steps, many boys and girls were already turning away with their newly blessed pets.

"We must hurry!" Juan walked a little faster, pulling Pedro along behind.

Juan worked his way to the second line, keeping his eye on the priest. He wanted to be sure and know when his turn came. Pedro must get a big blessing.

Pedro stood quietly in the sunshine. His eyes stared at a tall sombrero held right under his nose by an old man. Pedro reached out his neck. Crunch! Crunch! Pedro's mouth worked sideways, with a large piece of the straw hat hanging out.

"Robber!" the old man shouted. He hit Pedro with what was left of the sombrero.

Pedro backed away, then turned and jumped over the pool by the fountain. He disappeared around the corner in a clatter of hoofs.

Juan could have cried. So little time left! Well, at least his fat pink pig, Rosita, was at home in the yard. She might get a fair blessing.

Behind his house, Juan found his pink pig. If he had not known that Rosita was pink, he would never have guessed it now!

Up to her ears in mud, Rosita greeted Juan happily. "Oink, oink, oink," she grunted. She rolled over in the chocolate-brown mud.

"We don't have much time, Rosita," said Juan as he filled a bucket with water and set to work.

After washing Rosita, Juan rubbed her with yellow straw until she gleamed. He tied a blue cord around her left leg. Then he picked her up and raced back to the church.

At the church steps the crowd was almost gone. Only a few boys and girls were left.

Juan pushed up to the front. He would not miss out again. He put his pig down, but he held the cord tightly in his hand. This time he would not let his pet get away.

Rosita felt hot without her coat of mud. She looked this way and that for some shade. There was shade under the tall trees by the fountain, but here by the steps the sun beat down fiercely.

Rosita blinked her tiny eyes and twitched her nose. She smelled water! She gave a mighty and sudden pull, and the cord on her leg came untied.

Juan turned around in time to see his shiny Rosita do a flip-flop in the muddy water near the fountain. He shook his fist at her!

The priest began on the last row of pets, while Juan listened sadly to the blessing. He had no pet and no blessing either! The happy voices of children with their lucky pets rose in the hot afternoon sunshine.

Juan turned and walked away, too sad to notice the sun and shade on the stones of the wall. He did not even smell the sweet honeysuckle blooming there. Only his ears heard the blessings of St. Francis that were not for his pets. Why had this happened to him?

Something dropping from the branches overhead made him stop. There, on the low wall in the honeysuckle, lay a tiny baby bird. It was a hummingbird, smallest of all feathered creatures.

Juan picked up the tiny bird. It was like a small leaf in his hands. He looked up, but he could see no nest. Behind him came the sound of the priest's voice. Even as he turned around to run back to the church, Juan heard the bells. The blessing would soon be over.

With the small fluff of a bird in his hands, Juan ran up to the priest, who had already turned away from the steps.

71

"Please, Father. Won't you bless this baby hummingbird for me? Just a small little blessing for this tiny one?" he begged.

The priest had to lean over to see the little bird. Then he smiled and held up his right hand in the blessing of St. Francis.

Juan could not believe his ears. It was the very same prayer that he had heard over and over again that afternoon. Even for a little bit of a creature, St. Francis gave the same blessing. Why, these were the same words that his pets would have received at the church! Perhaps how big and important you were did not matter. Perhaps God loved every heart that beat. He would remember that.

Juan thanked the priest. He walked away from the church, a wide smile on his face. He smoothed the feathers of the tiny hummingbird with one finger.

"Small pet, big pet, my little one," Juan whispered, "it is all the same to St. Francis. Every bird and animal is his good friend."

IRENE TAMONY

72

St. Francis of Assisi

SISTER ST. AUBYN, C.S.J.　　　　　　　　　LORRAINE ERICKSON

1. St. Fran - cis loved the wind and rain,
2. St. Fran - cis found great peace and joy

He loved each lit - tle flow - er;
In do - ing things for oth - ers.

He loved the sun - shine and the storms
He called the lit - tle birds and beasts

Be - cause they show God's pow - er.
His sis - ters and his broth - ers.

73

Happy Hearts and Happy Faces

74

Music

Can you dance?
I love to dance!
Music is my happy chance.
Music playing
In the street
Gets into
My hands and feet.

Can you sing?
I love to sing!
Music, like a bird in Spring,
With a gold
And silver note
Gets into
My heart and throat.

Can you play?
I'd love to play!
Practice music every day—
Then you'll give
The world a chance
To dance and sing,
To sing and dance.

ELEANOR FARJEON

The Strange Wild Sound

Patrick and his mother and grandfather lived in a big apartment house in the City of New York.

One afternoon all the neighbors were surprised to hear a strange wild sound coming from somewhere in the apartment building.

Mrs. Simons opened her window. "What is it?" she shouted. "An air raid?"

The strange wild sound came again.

Mrs. La Rosa rushed to the street. "Is there a fire?" she cried.

The janitor came running to the door. "What's happening?" he shouted.

Children raced around the corner. Dogs barked, truck drivers stopped, and all the time the strange wild sound grew louder.

Mr. Hawkins, from the little store at the corner, stepped out to the street and looked up at the building.

"It's coming from the third floor," he said. "I'll go up there and find out what all this noise is about."

Mr. Hawkins didn't know that Patrick was learning, for the first time, how to play a bagpipe!

It was his birthday, and his grandfather had given him a bagpipe. It wasn't a very big bagpipe. It was not the size of the pipes that Grandfather had learned to play when he was a lad in Ireland. But Patrick knew that out of it would come the music his people loved so well.

Patrick's mother opened the door for Mr. Hawkins. "Were you frightened by the pipes?" she asked.

"What pipes?" asked Mr. Hawkins, thinking perhaps the water pipes had broken.

"Bagpipes," said Patrick. Patrick smiled and lifted the leather bag. With much blowing, he filled the bag with air. Again, the strange wild sound filled the apartment and the street below.

Grandfather came out of the kitchen. "Some day the lad will be able to play the old marching tunes as well as I can," he said proudly.

Mrs. Simons had followed Mr. Hawkins to the door. She was frowning. "How long will it take Patrick to learn to play?" she asked.

"He'll be able to play by St. Patrick's Day," said Grandfather.

"St. Patrick's Day!" cried Mrs. Simons. "That's almost a year away, isn't it? Will he be blowing and tooting all that time in this apartment?"

By this time Mrs. La Rosa, the janitor, and all the children had come to the door.

"This used to be a quiet place," sighed Mrs. La Rosa.

Patrick said nothing. He tried again, but he had no luck. The sound came loud and shrill, even wilder than before.

"I'll call the owner of the building," said the janitor.

"Indeed, you won't," replied Patrick's mother.

"Why not?" asked Mrs. Simons.

"The lad will learn to play the pipes at Shamrock Hall," said his mother. "He won't be bothering you."

That was the last time the pipes were heard on that street. From then on, until the night before St. Patrick's Day, Patrick tooted the toot in Shamrock Hall. His grandfather said that the Hall was the best place to learn to play the pipes.

"When it's done within a small place like an apartment," he told Patrick, "it's like caging a lion."

Then came St. Patrick's Day, a proud day in the life of the Irish. Young Patrick would march in the St. Patrick's Day parade with Grandfather and the other pipers. Patrick counted the minutes until the parade began.

At the signal from the leader of the pipers, he began to play. Up the wide street they marched. Crowds on the sidewalks cheered them on their way. A newspaperman rushed out and took a picture of Patrick.

"You're the youngest piper in the whole parade," he said. "Watch for tomorrow morning's paper. Your picture will be in it."

80

"What piece do we play next?" Patrick asked his grandfather, as they came near the big library.

"We'll be playing 'Where the Grass Grows Green'," said Grandfather, but he had no time to sing the words.

Patrick's face was blue from blowing on the pipes, and it was puffed out like a balloon. As he played he could see the men and women along the street. Some were crying, some were cheering, and some were singing, "Where the grass grows green."

It was a wonderful St. Patrick's Day! The sun was shining. The parade was miles long. Men from all over the city, from the counties of New York State, and other states too, marched to the music of the bands. Tramp! Tramp! came the sound of the marchers' feet.

81

They came at last to St. Patrick's Cathedral. There, on the steps, stood the Cardinal.

They all had been waiting for this moment. Young Patrick lifted his bagpipe. With the others he began to play:

> *All hail to St. Patrick,*
> *Who brought to old Ireland*
> *The faith that we love*
> *And we cherish today;*
> *In his land and our land,*
> *In good times and bad times,*
> *We honor his name*
> *As we praise and we pray.*

The Cardinal smiled, while the crowds cheered and the bells rang out. Then the Cardinal blessed the pipers, young and old.

"You'll never forget this day, my lad," said Patrick's grandfather as they marched toward the park.

"I'll come every year of my life," promised the boy, "as long as I am able to blow a bagpipe."

And who do you suppose rushed out to greet them at the end? You're right! Mrs. Simons, Mrs. La Rosa, Mr. Hawkins, the janitor, and all the children.

It was Mr. Hawkins who spoke first. "You were
wonderful, Patrick," he exclaimed.

They all laughed and clapped their hands. It had
taken time, but now they loved the strange wild sound
of an Irish bagpipe. And Patrick's mother? There she
stood, the proudest woman in the great City of New
York.

Nino and His Fish

The Wonderful Idea

Nino sat thinking. He was thinking about his birthday that was coming the next day. Nino knew there would be no birthday party. That is, there would be no party unless his father's luck changed.

Nino's father, Tony, was a fisherman. This year the salmon were late in coming and hard to catch. Nino knew that if a fisherman doesn't catch fish, he doesn't have money for birthdays.

Nino sat thinking. He smelled the salt smell of the sea. Then he suddenly jumped up and ran quickly into the house to find his mother.

"I have an idea," he cried. "A wonderful idea! What if my father would let me go fishing with him? What if I should go fishing and catch a fish of my own? A great big fish! Then I could invite all my friends, and we could eat fish at my birthday party."

Nino's mother looked at him gently and smiled.

"And you would not mind if you had no cake, Nino?" she asked. "I cannot buy eggs and butter and all the good things that go into a real birthday cake."

Nino was quiet for a moment, thinking about a birthday party without any birthday cake. Then he laughed. "Who cares about cake? Fish is fine for a birthday."

The next morning Nino was the first in the house to be awake. He begged his father to take him to the Fisherman's Wharf.

Nino loved the Fisherman's Wharf. He loved the smell of fish, the smell of new ropes, the paint smell of the boats, and the salt smell of the sea.

They passed the Fish Market with its rows of fish all spread out neatly on their beds of ice. Almost at the end of Fisherman's Wharf they came to a beautiful restaurant. It belonged to their friend Angelo.

This restaurant was no place for fishermen. It had been built for the tourists who came to visit Fisherman's Wharf.

This morning Angelo himself stood at the door of his fine restaurant. He waved at Tony and Nino.

"So you are now a fisherman?" he asked the boy.

Nino smiled. "Yes," he answered, "I am going fishing with my father to catch a big fish for my birthday today. I shall ask all my friends to come."

"Ho–ho–ho," laughed Angelo. "A fish for a birthday! Who would ever want fish for a birthday? You should have a cake."

Nino did not know how to answer. How could he tell Angelo his father had no money for a cake?

Angelo must have seen that his laughing had hurt Nino's feelings. He hurried after the boy and gave Nino a little package of fresh little white fish for bait.

"Good luck," he said, and Nino thanked him.

The fishing boats were beginning to leave the harbor. Nino and his father reached their boat, called the *Santa Rosa*, and soon it started chug–chugging out of the harbor. When they came to the best place to catch the salmon, Nino picked up his long rod. He untied the package of bait and quickly had one of the little white fish on his hook.

All the rest of the morning Nino waited and watched his line, but no salmon came.

"Oh, please, salmon," Nino half whispered to himself. "Please, salmon, come up and hook yourself tight so that I can have a birthday party."

But no salmon came on his hook.

The sun grew hot. The boy and his father ate the little food they had brought with them. Then Nino grew sleepy. The sea was so shiny with all the sun.

He was almost asleep when suddenly he felt a sharp tug, and his line started to go out fast. Nino jumped up. How could he hold tight enough? Was this a whale?

Then he saw it. There it was! A monster fish all right! Nino burst out laughing with excitement.

"Ho–ho–ho! fishy! Ho–ho, my fish! Come, come now! Slowly . . . slowly! There, forward . . . now back. Now I have you!"

Nino brought in his line. He could feel that the great fish was tired. Slowly. Slowly. Then . . . quick to the side of the boat.

Nino's father reached down in the water and hooked the fish with a long iron hook.

"What a monster!" cried Nino's father as he looked at the great fish lying in the *Santa Rosa*.

Nino could hardly believe his luck.

Happy Birthday

No more salmon came their way that day. Soon the cold gray fog rolled in from the sea, and the faraway fog horn blew "Whoo–oo." Then Tony knew it was time to go home. The other fishing boats turned toward home too. They all chugged quietly through the gray fog into the harbor.

When Nino and his father passed the pink doors of the restaurant, Angelo came out.

"What a fine fisherman you have, Tony!" he said.

Tony looked proudly at Nino and then at the great fish. "Yes," he said, "Nino caught the biggest fish of all the fishermen."

"I could use a fish like that," said Angelo. "The tourists would like it. I'll tell you what I'll do. I'll buy that fish, and I'll give a birthday party for Nino here at my restaurant."

Nino could hardly believe his ears. He, Nino, to have a birthday party at Angelo's! He could not speak, but when his father nodded and smiled Nino gave Angelo the fish.

"Fine!" laughed Angelo. "Now go and ask every one of your friends."

90

Nino rushed about asking all of his friends from school and many of the fishermen. Then he ran home to tell his mother to hurry back to Angelo's.

The pink doors of Angelo's restaurant were wide open, and right in the middle of the front window was Nino's fish. His great big beautiful fish! The wonderful fish that Nino had caught by himself! Below it Angelo had put a sign.

Nino could hardly believe his eyes when he saw this. He could hardly believe his ears when he heard Angelo talking to the tourists.

"No," said Angelo, "I can't serve you tonight. Come tomorrow, and I will cook the big fish for you. Tonight I have invited only the little fisherman and his friends."

What a feast! The best food in the city was offered to Nino and his friends. When this was finished, everyone was quiet.

"Oh—o—o!" gasped Nino, as Angelo himself came in from the kitchen carrying the most beautiful cake in the world. There were three layers, and on the very top was a great fish made of blue icing with birthday candles sparkling around it.

It was all so gay, and the cake was so beautiful, that everyone began to sing as Nino cut the first piece. After the cake was eaten, every bit of it, the friends of Nino began to sing and dance. They danced and they danced.

They even danced all the way home. All the way up the Fisherman's Wharf! All the way through the dark little streets, and all the way to their houses. Nino never stopped dancing until at last his mother kissed him and sent him to bed.

EDITH THACHER HURD

House on the Hill

Higgity, biggity,
diggity dill,
a little round house
sits on a high hill.
It sits on the hill
like a hat on a head,
the roof has a peak and
the chimney is red.
And just like a feather
on somebody's hat,
the smoke curls up
as jaunty as that.
At night two windows
are two yellow eyes,
like somebody staring
in mild surprise.

Figgity, tiggity,
wiggity will,
I'll save up my dimes
and my pennies until
I can live on that hill.
Then I'll look down,
out of those windows
over the town.
The smoke will curl
and the windows blink.
Folk will stare
and I shall wink.
O, diggity dill,
that house on the hill,
I can see me there now
at the window sill.

NORA S. UNWIN

Where Did That Bird Go?

Once, in a busy Dollar Store, there was a row of bird cages, and each one held a pretty yellow bird. On each cage there was a sign which said, "Singing Canary: $1.00." That is, each cage except the last one. In the last cage sat Trilly.

Trilly had a beautiful voice, but no one at the store had ever heard him sing because he just didn't feel like singing. Trilly needed a home. When the store manager saw that Trilly did not sing like the other canaries, he marked him down. So the sign on the last cage said, "Canary: 39¢."

One day, four blocks up the street from the Dollar
Store, a girl was practicing her piano lesson. Her
name was Kathy, and she would rather do anything
else than practice—even wash dishes.

Kathy was trying to learn a piece called "Dolly's
Dance," because her grandma was coming for a visit
at the end of the week and Grandma had played the
"Dolly's Dance" when she was a little girl.

Kathy practiced and looked at the clock. She
dusted the piano keys and looked at the clock. She
looked out of the window and looked at the clock.
Then she played the tune with one finger.

"That is not very good," called Mother from the kitchen. "Maybe you'd better rest a while. You may go to the Dollar Store for me. I need another cake pan like my round one."

Kathy would have been glad to visit the Dollar Store for no reason at all, but today she was very glad to go. She put on her hat and coat, kissed her mother good-by, and went skipping off to the store.

It was filled with people. Kathy bought a round cake pan for Mother. Then she looked at the dolls on the next counter. The tiny ones were only a dime, but Kathy didn't have a dime to spend.

Before leaving the store, she walked back to look at the singing birds. All down the line she went, speaking to each canary. At last she came to Trilly.

"Poor little bird, can't you sing?" asked Kathy.

Trilly put his head on one side, then on the other side. Then he hopped lightly down from his perch. Two boys came along just then.

"Hey! look at this bird, only thirty-nine cents!" said the bigger boy. As he spoke the boy stuck his finger between the bars of the little door of the cage. Then, when he pulled out his finger, the door opened and out came Trilly!

The three children stood there, staring at the open
door.   Before anyone could move, Trilly flew up, up,
up.   He began flying around and around, as if he
might be looking for a way out into the world.

"Bird out!   Bird out!" all the children screamed.

The clerks ran around, trying to get Trilly to come
down.   The store manager came and looked at the row
of cages.

"It's only that thirty-nine-cent bird," he said.
"Never mind.   He will come down sometime."

98

It was exciting, waiting there in the store for the little bird to come back, but Kathy knew that she should get home to her practicing.

"I'll wait just five minutes more," she thought. It would be fun to see the bird walk into his little cage.

But no one saw Trilly come back to his cage. In a minute he flew down and lighted on a great pile of fruit in the store window. Next, he perched for a second on the shoulder of a boy, who stood there with his mouth wide open. Then in the excitement Trilly disappeared!

The ladies in the store looked in their shopping bags. The clerks looked under the counters. No Trilly. Finally everyone gave up looking.

When Kathy reached home, her mother said, "I thought you were lost."

"I wasn't lost, but a dear little bird is lost, and no one knows where he went," said Kathy as she put her hat on the piano.

Then she told Mother the whole story of what had happened. After that she sat down to practice.

Teedle, teedle, ping, ping, ping, went the "Dolly's Dance." And then, suddenly through the room, a song began—the cheerful whistling of a bird!

"Mother!" called Kathy, "my hat is singing!"

Mother came from the kitchen and looked at the hat. There was Trilly standing on it. His eyes were sparkling, and he was singing happily.

"Look," said Mother, "his feet are caught in the ribbon."

"Tweet, tweet, trill!" sang Trilly, because he felt at home.

Mother herself then went to the Dollar Store. She paid the manager thirty-nine cents for the bird and bought a cage for Trilly. How surprised the store people were to hear that Trilly had been worn away on a hat!

When Mother got home from the store, Kathy was practicing and Trilly was singing "Dolly's Dance." At least, that's what Kathy decided he was singing.

And when Grandma arrived for her visit a few days later, she said that she had never heard the "Dolly's Dance" played better in all her life.

CLAIRE TRASK

100

My Valentine

I have a little valentine
   That someone sent to me.
It's pink and white and red and blue,
   And pretty as can be.

Forget-me-nots are round the edge,
   And tiny roses, too;
And such a lovely piece of lace—
   The very palest blue.

And in the center there's a heart,
   As red as red can be!
And on it's written all in gold,
   "To You, with love from Me."

MARY CATHERINE PARSONS

101

Valentines for America

Anya could hardly wait to get home from school to tell Mama all about the valentines. But she stood for a minute at the turn in the road and admired the house where she and Mama and Papa lived. To everybody else it might look like nothing but an old gray farmhouse, but to Anya it was the most wonderful house in the world.

America, thought Anya, was wonderful, even if the children at school sometimes laughed at her. Before long, she thought, they would not laugh, because she would do everything the American way. And she was going to start right now with the valentines.

"Mama!" Anya hurried into the house. "Mama, could Papa maybe take me to town in the truck to buy valentines?"

There was no answer, but in the kitchen was a note saying that Mama had gone with Papa to take the pigs to market. Mama went whenever she could, because she got lonely, with no friends to talk to.

"Mama's different, too," thought Anya, "and doesn't speak American so well yet." Then she remembered! "Oh, the valentines!"

The valentine box, gay with red and white paper, had been a surprise to Anya. Teacher had brought it into the school this morning, and, by listening to what the others said, Anya learned that tomorrow would be Valentine's Day. Everybody would bring valentines and push them through the slot in the top of the pretty box.

Anya had stood quietly beside Teacher after school, waiting until she was told she could speak.

"Where do you buy valentines, please?"

"At the ten-cent store in town, Anya," Teacher had said kindly. "A penny each, most of them. Or you can make pretty ones of your own out of red and white paper. They're fun to make."

"Yes, Teacher. Thank you, please."

The children had laughed, and Anya had turned bright red. It was so hard to remember not to say "thank you" and "please" at once.

"Should I buy a valentine for everybody in the room?" Anya asked George, the friendly bus driver, who took her home the last of all.

"If you want to," said George. "Do what you please. It's a free country."

"Better if I do buy for all," Anya decided. "Even the ones who laugh. They teach me what I do wrong, so I don't do it again."

But now, sitting in the empty kitchen, Anya felt that everything would be wrong tomorrow. If she had nothing to put in the box, the children would think she did not like American ways.

"I could maybe walk to town," Anya thought. But a look at the clock told her that she could not. It was six miles to town, and the stores would be closed before Anya could get there. "Or I could try to make some valentines the way Teacher said."

The trouble was that she had no red paper. She had no paper at all except her yellow school tablet with the green lines across it.

Anya got herself a glass of milk, spread a thick slice of homemade bread with Mama's good butter, and sat down to think.

Mama said that food made everything look brighter. Anya could remember how it felt to be hungry all the time in the old country.

It was different here in America, of course. Everybody ate three meals a day and as much as he wanted.

The first things Mama had bought with part of Papa's first pay were kitchen things—cooky and cake pans.

"Plain eating is nice," said Mama, "but pretty tastes twice as good."

And so Mama's cakes and cookies were always frosted with little rosebuds, names, and, on Christmas, a beautiful red Santa Claus.

106

Anya fixed herself another slice of bread and butter.

"Christmas wrappings!" she thought suddenly. "Maybe some of the plain red paper will do." She hunted for it.

But Mama was too neat. The plain red paper had already been cleared out, and nothing was left but some paper with Christmas bells all over it. Anya went back to her bread and butter.

"There must be some way," she told the fat black-and-white cat, who came rubbing around her legs. "Papa says there is always a way, if only you think hard enough."

Anya had supper almost ready when Mama and Papa came in, rubbing their cold hands.

Mama sniffed happily. "Smells good."

"Mama thinks the best thing about America is food," Papa teased.

"Second best, maybe," said Mama cheerfully. "First is doing what you please."

"That's what George said." Anya set the fried potatoes and the good pink ham on the table. "Papa, I have an American thing to do before tomorrow and nothing to do it with."

"Nothing?" Papa smiled at her. "Nobody ever has nothing. Maybe you should think harder."

Mama cut the big cake which she had baked that morning. It had a red rose and beautiful green frosting leaves on it.

"It's too pretty to eat, almost," said Anya. "Like a picture."

But she was not thinking much about the cake. She was thinking about valentines. Anya's thoughts wandered all over the house, upstairs and down, and found nothing to use for valentines. Her thoughts came back to the kitchen again.

"Papa!" cried Anya suddenly. "I thought harder."

Next morning Anya got on the bus, carrying a large package neatly wrapped in brown paper.

"What's in it?" everybody asked.

"Valentines," Anya answered proudly.

"Must be big ones," somebody said. "They may not even go in the valentine box."

Anya said nothing. Even if her valentines were not like American ones, they were the best she could do. Anyway, George had certainly said, "Do as you please. It's a free country." Now was as good a time as any to find out if this was really true.

Anya marched into school and handed the teacher her package.

"Are these your valentines, Anya? Put them in the valentine box, please," said Teacher.

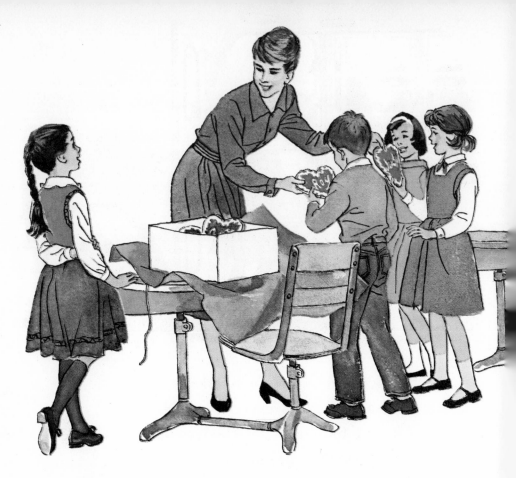

"They won't go in the box." Anya could feel herself getting red again. "Will you open them for me?"

Teacher looked surprised and opened Anya's package. The children crowded around as she lifted out big heart-shaped cookies frosted in red. In the middle of each cooky, with letters of white frosting, was the name of a child. There was a cooky for every child in the room.

Teacher smiled at Anya as she called out the names. "You must tell your mother and father how glad we are to have such fine new Americans in our country."

Anya smiled happily. "Oh, thank you, please," she said.

But none of the children laughed this time. They were much too busy eating Anya's Valentines for America.

MILDRED LAWRENCE

Once Upon a Time Tales

Happily Ever After

Stories are
A joy to me—
Merry tales—all bright
With laughter.

But best of all
Are those that end:
"And they lived happily
Ever after!"

ILO ORLEANS

The Bremen Band

Once upon a time there was a donkey that had worked for his master for many years. When, at last, the donkey grew so old that he could no longer work, his master wished to get rid of him.

The donkey, fearing that he might be killed, ran away. He took the road to the city of Bremen where he had often heard a street band playing. Since the donkey liked music, he thought he might join the band.

He had not gone far when he came upon an old dog who was panting as if he were very tired.

"Why are you panting so, my friend?" asked the donkey.

"Ah," said the dog, "I am too old to hunt any longer. My master wishes to have me killed, and so I have run away. But how I am to find bread and meat, I do not know."

"Well," said the donkey, "come with me. I am going to play in the band at Bremen. I think you and I can easily earn a living through music. I can play the fiddle, and you can play the drum."

The dog was quite willing, and he walked on with
the donkey. They had not gone far when they saw
a cat, looking as sad as three days of rainy weather.

"What's the matter with you, old Tom?" asked the
donkey. "Why are you so sad?"

"You would be sad, too," said the cat, "if you were
in my place. Since I am getting old and cannot catch
mice, my master wishes to drown me. I have run
away. But how I am going to live, I do not know."

"Come with us to Bremen," said the donkey. "We
are going to play in the band. I know you love music,
for you sing so well at night. You too can join the
band."

"That is just what I should like to do," said the cat.

So the donkey, the dog, and the cat all walked on together. After some time the three came to a farmyard. There on the gate perched a rooster, crowing "cock-a-doodle-doo" with all his might.

"Why are you making so much noise at this time of day?" asked the donkey.

"Ah," said the rooster, "I find I must have my head cut off so that I may be served for dinner on Monday. I'm crowing as hard as I can while my head is still on."

"Come with us, old Red Comb," said the donkey. "We are going to Bremen to join the band. You have a fine voice. You can join, too."

"Ah," said the rooster, "that is just what I should like to do."

So they all went on their way to Bremen.

By evening the four friends came to some woods where they stopped for the night. The donkey and the dog lay down under a large tree. The cat climbed up on one of the branches. The rooster flew to the very top of the tree where he felt quite safe. From his perch on the top of the tree the rooster saw a light.

Calling to his friends, he said, "We are not far from a house. I can see a light."

"Let's go on," said the donkey, "for it may be just the house for us."

As they came near the house, the light grew larger and brighter. Because he was the tallest, the donkey went up to the window and looked in.

"What do you see, old Long Ears?" asked the rooster.

"What do I see?" answered the donkey. "Why, I see a table spread with plenty to eat and drink, and I see robbers sitting around the table. They are having their supper."

"We should be there, too, if we had our rights," said the rooster.

"Ah, yes," said the donkey. "If we could only get rid of the robbers!"

Then the four friends talked over what they could do to drive the robbers out of the house. At last they decided what to do. The donkey stood upon his hind legs and placed his front feet on the window sill. The dog then stood on the donkey's back. The cat climbed upon the dog, while the rooster perched upon the cat's head.

When the donkey gave a signal, they began—all at the same time—to make their loudest music. The donkey brayed, the dog barked, the cat mewed, and the rooster crowed, all with such great force that the window shook so that it was almost broken.

118

The robbers had never heard such a noise. They thought it must have come from witches or some other horrible creatures. They all ran at once, as fast as they could, to the woods behind the house.

The four friends, seeing their chance, rushed in and ate what the robbers had left upon the table. It did not take long, for they acted as if they had been hungry for a month.

After the four had eaten, they put out the light. Then each one went to sleep in the spot which he liked best. The donkey lay down in the yard. The dog lay behind the door. The cat curled himself up in front of the fireplace, while the rooster flew up to the rooftop. They soon fell fast asleep.

When all was still and the light was out, the robber chief sent one of his bravest men back to the house. The man found the house very quiet, and so he walked in and started to light a candle.

Seeing the great shining eyes of the cat, he thought they were live coals. Hoping to get a light, he held the candle close to the cat's eyes. This made the cat so angry that he flew up fiercely and scratched the man's face. This frightened the robber so much that he started running for the door.

As he went by, the dog jumped up and bit him on the leg. In the yard the robber ran into the donkey, who gave him a great kick. The rooster on the roof was awakened by the noise and cried, "Cock-a-doodle-doo, cock-a-doodle-doo!"

120

As fast as his legs could carry him, the man ran back to the robber chief.

"Ah," he cried to his chief, "in that house there is a terrible witch, who flew at me and scratched my face with her long, sharp nails. By the door stood a man with a knife, who cut me in the leg. Out in the yard lay a great black creature, who hit me with his wooden club. Upon the roof sat the judge who cried, 'What did he do? Put him in the stew.' When I heard this, I ran off as fast as I could."

The robbers were so frightened at this news that they ran away and never again went near the house in the woods.

The four friends liked the place so well that they never went to Bremen. They stayed in the little house, and, so far as I know, they are there to this day.

RETOLD FROM GRIMM

The Real Princess

There was once a prince who wished to marry a princess. But she was to be a *real* princess, mind you. And indeed, real princesses were hard to find, as you might imagine.

The prince had traveled all over the world to find one, but nowhere could he see what he was looking for. There were many princesses, it is true, but it was hard to tell which were real ones. There was always something about each one that was not just as it should be.

After a long time the prince returned home. He was very sad, for he wished so much to find a real princess. The old king and queen were sad, too, for they wished their son to be happy.

One evening there was a dreadful storm. The rain poured down, and the wind blew fiercely. It was a fearful night indeed.

In the middle of the storm there came a loud knocking at the palace gate. The old king himself went out and opened it.

There at the gate stood a princess. But, oh dear, what a state she was in from the wind and the rain! The water dripped from her hair and her clothes. It ran in at the toes of her shoes and out at the heels. And yet, looking as she did, the girl said that she was a real princess.

"Well, we shall soon find out," thought the old queen, but she said not one word.

The queen went into a bedroom and took everything off the bed. She placed a small green pea on the framework of the bed. She then took twenty mattresses and laid them upon the small pea. On top of the mattresses she piled twenty feather beds. The princess lay on this high bed the whole night.

124

In the morning she was asked how she had slept.

"Oh, most horribly!" replied the princess. "I hardly closed my eyes all night! I'm sure I do not know what was in the bed, but I was lying upon something ever so hard. It has made me black and blue all over. It is quite dreadful!"

"Ah!" said the old queen. "Now I know you are a real princess. You felt one small pea through twenty mattresses and twenty feather beds. No one but a real princess is so tender as that."

So the prince took the girl for his wife, for he knew that at last he had found a real princess.

The pea was put into a beautiful glass case in the palace, where it is still to be seen, if no one has stolen it away.

And this, mind you, is a real story.

HANS CHRISTIAN ANDERSEN

The Ant and the Grasshopper

Once an ant and a grasshopper lived in the same meadow. The ant was busy laying up food for the winter.

"Why do you work so hard?" asked the grasshopper. "Just look at me. I don't work. I dance and sing and have a good time."

"Yes, I see that you do," said the ant. "But if I played all summer, what should I do for food in the winter?"

The grasshopper laughed. "Oh, winter is a long way off," he said. "I never think about that." Then he danced merrily away.

After a time the summer was gone. The ground was white with snow. The ant was snug and warm in her little house, and it was full of food. But the poor grasshopper had no home. He had no food. He was stiff with cold, and oh, so hungry!

"Dear me," he said. "What shall I do? I am very cold, and I can find no grass to eat. Maybe the ant will help me. I will go and ask her."

So he looked all about for the ant's house. When he found it, he called to her, "Please, dear Ant, may I come in? I am very cold and hungry."

"Poor Grasshopper!" said the ant. "Come in and have some bread. You laughed at me for working. You danced and played all summer long. If you had worked then, you would not be asking for food now."

"That is so," said the grasshopper. "And I am sorry. Thank you for the bread. Good-by."

Out into the cold he went.

And the ant never saw him again.

AESOP

Silly Jack

Once upon a time there was a lad whose name was Jack. He lived alone with his mother. Jack was a kind lad, but he was so lazy that he would do nothing but lie in the sun during the hot summer and sit by the corner of the fireplace during the cold winter.

Now, Jack's mother worked very hard. She made her living by spinning wool. At last the poor woman could stand Jack's laziness no longer. She told him that he would have to leave their home and live as he could unless he began to work for a living.

128

So Jack went out and hired himself for a day's work to a farmer for a penny. Never having had any money before, Jack lost the penny when he crossed a brook on his way home.

"You stupid boy," said Jack's mother when she heard how he had lost his money. "You should have put it in your pocket."

"I'll do so another time," said Jack.

The next day Jack went out again and hired himself to a cow keeper, who gave him a jar of milk for his day's work. Jack put the jar of milk into the large pocket of his jacket, spilling it all long before he got home.

"Dear me," said his mother upon hearing this, "you should have carried it on your head."

"I'll do so another time," said Jack.

129

The next day Jack hired himself again to a farmer, who gave him cream cheese for his work. In the evening Jack started home with the cream cheese on his head. By the time he got home, the cheese had melted—part of it being lost and part of it still running down his face and neck.

"You silly lad!" cried his mother. "You should have carried it ever so carefully in your hands."

"I'll do so another time," said Jack.

The next day Jack again went out to work. This time he hired himself to a baker, who would give him nothing for his work but a large cat. Jack took the cat and started home, carrying the cat ever so carefully in his hands. In only a short time the cat had scratched Jack so badly that he had to let it go.

When he got home, his mother said to him, "You foolish fellow, you should have tied it with a string and dragged it along after you."

"I'll do so another time," said Jack.

The next day Jack hired himself to a butcher, who gave him for his work a big leg of lamb. Jack took the lamb, tied it to a string, and dragged it along after him in the dirt. Indeed, by the time he got home the meat was not fit for use.

This time Jack's mother was quite out of patience with him, for the next day was Sunday, and now they would have only cabbage for their dinner.

"You silly of sillies," cried she to her son, "you should have carried it on your shoulder."

"I'll do so another time," said Jack.

On Monday Jack went once more and hired himself, this time to a cattle keeper. He was given a donkey for his work. Although Jack was very strong, he found it hard to lift the donkey to his shoulders. At last he did so and began walking slowly home with his heavy prize.

Now, it happened that on his way home he passed the house of a rich man. The man lived there with his only daughter—a beautiful girl, but one who could not hear or speak. The girl had never in her life been able to laugh or say even one word. The doctors said she would never be well until someone made her laugh.

This young girl was looking out the window when Jack passed with the donkey on his shoulders, its legs sticking up in the air. The sight was so strange and funny that the girl broke out into great fits of laughter. At once she could speak and hear.

This filled the rich man with such joy that he allowed his daughter to marry Jack. Jack became a rich gentleman. And so it was that Jack, his mother, and his beautiful wife lived together in a large house in great happiness for the rest of their days.

ENGLISH FOLK TALE

The Owl and the Pussy-Cat

The Owl and the Pussy-Cat went to sea
   In a beautiful pea-green boat:
They took some honey, and plenty of money
   Wrapped up in a five-pound note.
The Owl looked up to the stars above,
   And sang to a small guitar,
"O lovely Pussy, O Pussy, my love,
   What a beautiful Pussy you are,
       You are,
       You are!
   What a beautiful Pussy you are!"

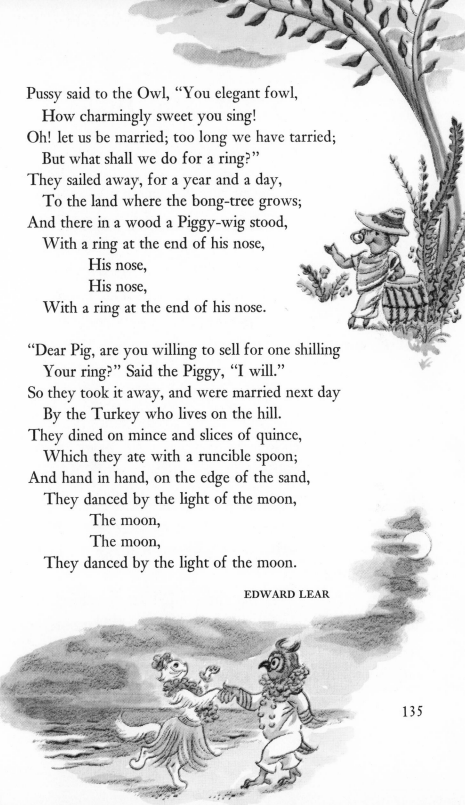

Pussy said to the Owl, "You elegant fowl,
  How charmingly sweet you sing!
Oh! let us be married; too long we have tarried;
  But what shall we do for a ring?"
They sailed away, for a year and a day,
  To the land where the bong-tree grows;
And there in a wood a Piggy-wig stood,
  With a ring at the end of his nose,
        His nose,
        His nose,
  With a ring at the end of his nose.

"Dear Pig, are you willing to sell for one shilling
  Your ring?" Said the Piggy, "I will."
So they took it away, and were married next day
  By the Turkey who lives on the hill.
They dined on mince and slices of quince,
  Which they ate with a runcible spoon;
And hand in hand, on the edge of the sand,
  They danced by the light of the moon,
        The moon,
        The moon,
  They danced by the light of the moon.

EDWARD LEAR

135

Beauty and the Beast

The Troubles of the Merchant

There was once a very rich merchant who owned much land and many ships. These ships traveled to faraway countries and brought back great riches. The man also had three sons and three beautiful daughters. Indeed, because their father was so rich, these children were used to having everything that money could buy.

One sad day the merchant lost his mighty fortune. All that was left was a small piece of land and a little house far from the town.

When the family was settled in the country, the father and his three sons set to work in the fields. His three daughters worked in the house. They found this very hard because they had never before worked. They were very unhappy over the loss of their fine clothes and gay parties, and they spent much of their time weeping.

Only the youngest daughter tried to be cheerful, and she often sang while doing her chores. Her sisters could not understand how she could be happy with such a poor life. They thought that she was silly.

Indeed, the two older girls were jealous of their sister because of her great beauty. She was so beautiful that she had always been called "Beauty."

After two years, when the family was beginning to get used to their poor life, they received surprising news. Their father found out that one of his ships, which he believed to be lost, had safely reached a harbor.

He prepared to leave at once to claim his riches. His children were wild with joy, believing that their poor life was at an end. The two older girls begged their father to bring them jewels and many fine dresses. Beauty, not wishing to trouble her father, asked only for a rose.

The merchant set off on his long journey. When he reached the harbor he found that his ship, and everything in it, had been lost in a fire. He started to return home, as poor as he had come.

He was within thirty miles of home when, in the middle of a large forest, he was caught in a heavy snowstorm. The poor merchant lost his way and began to fear that he should die of hunger and cold. Suddenly he saw a light. As he came nearer he found that the light came from a beautiful palace.

The merchant walked into the palace. Although he saw no one, everything he needed appeared before him. There was food, a warm fire, and even a place to sleep.

It was very late the next morning when the merchant awakened. To his surprise, he found a new suit of clothes in place of his own old torn ones.

"Certainly," he said to himself, "this palace must belong to some good fairy who has seen and felt sorry for my misfortunes."

The merchant then prepared to start out on his journey home. He walked out of the palace. Instead of seeing a garden covered with snow, he saw plants covered with blooming flowers.

Passing through the beautiful garden, he remembered his promise to Beauty and started picking several roses. At that moment he heard a loud roar. He saw moving fiercely toward him so frightful a beast that the poor merchant was ready to die of fear.

"You are a thankless man," cried the beast in a most horrible voice. "I have saved your life by letting you stay in my palace. In return, you are stealing my beautiful roses. Ah, you shall not go unpunished for such an act! You shall die for it."

The unhappy merchant threw himself on his knees before the beast and cried, "Oh, please forgive me, my lord. I did not mean to hurt your feelings by taking roses for one of my dear daughters."

139

The beast was thoughtful for a moment. Then he said, "If you will give me one of your daughters, you shall not be killed. If not, you must promise that you will yourself return to my palace within three months."

Because the merchant had no idea of giving up one of his daughters, he promised to return.

Before the beast disappeared, he said, "You may leave when you please, but you need not go empty-handed. Go back to the room in which you slept. There you will see a large chest. Fill it with whatever you like best."

Even though he had a chest filled with gold pieces, the merchant left the palace feeling sadder than he had upon arriving there.

Instead of greeting his children with joy, he stared sadly at them. Holding out the roses, he said, "Here, Beauty, these are for you. You little know how much they have cost your poor father."

The two older daughters cried loudly when they heard of their father's misfortune.

"If Beauty had not asked for a rose, this would not have happened," they said. "Now she will cause the death of our poor father. And yet she sheds not one tear."

140

"Why should I?" said Beauty. "It would be useless. The beast agreed to take one of the daughters. I will happily give myself up to save my father's life."

At once her father said that he could not allow this. But Beauty said over and over that she wanted to go. Finally, with sadness, her father agreed to take Beauty to the palace of the beast.

When the sad day came, Beauty set out with her father. They found the palace as brightly lighted as before. The merchant and his daughter went into the great hall, where they found a table, set for two people, and loaded with all kinds of delicious foods.

After they had eaten, they heard a terrible noise. In a moment the beast entered. Indeed, Beauty was frightened of the horrible form, but she tried to hide her fear.

"Good evening, Beauty," said the beast in a most horrible voice. "Have you come here willingly?"

"Yes," she replied shakily.

"You are very good, and my thanks are deeply felt," growled the beast. And to her father he said, "As for you, my good man, you are to leave tomorrow and never return. Good night!"

Beauty's Life in the Palace

After Beauty went to sleep that night, she dreamed that a very handsome prince came to her and said, "Do not be afraid, dear Beauty. You shall be treated kindly. But do not put faith only in what you see with your eyes. Remember my words, Beauty."

Beauty told this dream to her father in the morning. It made him feel a little better, but he was weeping when he said good-by to his daughter.

After he had left, Beauty began looking at the many rooms of the palace. How surprised she was when she came to a door over which was written, "Beauty's Room!" Opening the door, she found all the lovely treasures that any girl could want. What delighted her most was a library with many beautiful books.

How surprised she was upon opening one book!   In it she found, in letters of gold, these words:

> "*Welcome, Beauty! do not fear!*
> *You are queen and mistress here:*
> *Speak your wishes, speak your will—*
> *You will find them granted still.*"

"Ah," sighed she, "there is nothing I wish so much as to see my dear father."

She turned toward a large mirror that was hanging near her.   There she saw her father arriving home sadly.   Her sisters were running out to meet him. Then the picture in the mirror disappeared, but Beauty felt very thankful to the beast that her wish had been granted.

That evening as Beauty sat down to supper, the
beast came and asked her if he might sit with her at the
table. Although she was frightened, she tried not to
show it and said not unkindly, "Do as you please."

"No," replied the beast in his horrible voice. "You
alone are mistress here. You need only tell me to go
if I bother you. I should be very hurt if you were not
happy."

The lovely girl could do no other than ask the
creature to stay. Soon he asked her if she did not think
him very ugly.

"Yes," said Beauty in a gentle manner, "but I think
you are very kind, too."

They talked for some time, and Beauty found her fear of him almost gone. Then suddenly the beast asked, "Beauty, will you marry me?"

Beauty was so surprised and frightened that she could hardly speak. She feared her answer would anger the beast, but she said bravely, "Oh, no! Beast."

"Then, good night, Beauty," said the beast sadly and he left the room.

Beauty could not help feeling sorry for him. That night she dreamed again of the unknown prince. This time she could not understand what he meant when he said, "Ah, Beauty, why are you so unkind to me? Must I be unhappy always?"

The days passed quickly enough for Beauty in the lovely palace. Every evening the beast appeared at suppertime, and Beauty enjoyed their talks together. She even began to look forward to his visits. She had become used to his ugliness and found him very kind and interesting.

There was but one thing that bothered her. Every night before the beast left he asked her to become his wife. One night she said to him, "Beast, you make me unhappy, for I can only offer you my friendship. I cannot love you."

Then he begged her for only one thing—that she would never leave him. But Beauty had seen in the mirror that day that her father was ill. Since his three sons and two daughters were married, he was alone. Beauty told the beast that she should die if he refused to let her go to her dear father.

"I may die of sorrow if you should stay away for a long time," said the beast. "But I should rather die than make you unhappy. You shall be with your father tomorrow morning."

Beauty promised to return in a week. The beast told her that she had only to wish herself back to the palace and she would be there.

When Beauty awakened the next morning, she found herself in her father's cottage. His delight at seeing her soon made him well again.

Beauty was so happy to be with her father that she could not wish herself back to the palace, and so she stayed longer than she had planned.

Then one night Beauty dreamed that she saw the beast lying half-dead on a path in the palace garden. Awaking in tears, she remembered that she had not kept her promise. She felt sorry that she had not been more thankful for the many kindnesses that the beast had shown her. At once Beauty wished herself back to the palace. When she woke the next morning, she was overjoyed to find herself there.

All day Beauty waited for the beast to appear. Then, remembering her dream, she ran to the garden. She found the path she had seen in her dream, and there lay the poor beast half-dead. Forgetting his great ugliness, Beauty ran to the creature.

The young girl got water from the spring and cried as she poured it over the beast's head.

Finally the beast opened his eyes and said faintly, "You forgot your promise to me. I did not care to live without you."

"Oh, you shall not die, dear Beast!" cried Beauty, "for I love you and want to be your wife."

She had hardly spoken these words when a flash of light streamed from the palace windows, fireworks were seen everywhere, and music sounded all around them. Beauty turned to the beast to ask what had happened, but he had disappeared. In his place stood the prince of her dreams—the one she had loved so long.

"Where is my poor beast?" asked Beauty eagerly.

"I am he," replied the prince. "A witch made me stay in the form of a beast until some beautiful girl should love me and promise to marry me."

And so the young prince and Beauty were married the very next day and lived happily for many, many long years.

FRENCH FAIRY TALE

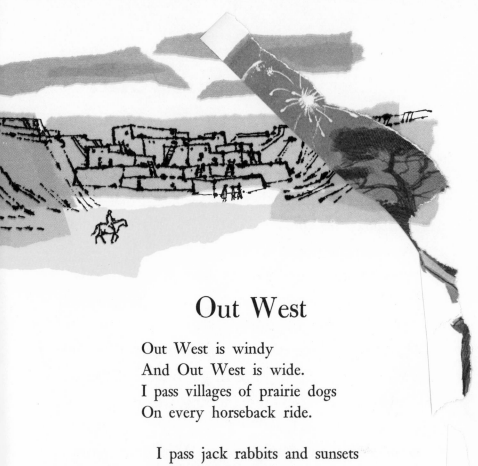

Out West

Out West is windy
And Out West is wide.
I pass villages of prairie dogs
On every horseback ride.

I pass jack rabbits and sunsets
And pueblo Indians,
And Mexicans in great big hats,
And they are all my friends.

But when the moon comes sliding
And sagebrush turns to foam,
Then outdoors is Out West,
But indoors is Home.

POLLY CHASE BOYDEN

Snowdrift

This was going to be the happiest birthday ever for David. Long ago his father had promised that on his next birthday he could choose, for his very own, a colt from all the horses on the ranch.

David sat up in bed sleepily and rubbed his eyes. Then he remembered what day this was, and he hopped out on the cold floor.

"Hurry up and get dressed," his father called. "It's snowing a little. We'll have to get out on the north range, where the horses are wintering, before the snow begins coming down hard."

David pulled on a warm wool shirt, heavy pants, wool socks, and his beautiful cowboy boots. Then he ran downstairs to breakfast.

"Happy birthday," said his mother.

After breakfast she helped him into his warm leather jacket. "Hurry home," she said. "There'll be ice cream and birthday cake when you get back."

It was cold out. The winter's first heavy snow had fallen, and the drifts lay deep in the gullies.

David and his father rode over the frozen ground and through the deep snow-filled gullies to the north range. Finally they found the horses, standing close together near a cliff.

David turned in the saddle and looked at the many horses and the frisky young colts, running and jump-ing playfully in the snow.

"Well, son," said David's father, "do you think you can choose the one you want?"

David grinned and rode slowly among the horses. Some turned and ran away. Others stood still, looking at the boy with interest. Then a few of the colts dashed around the cliff, and David followed, hoping to find his own special colt among them.

Suddenly David heard the whinny of a frightened animal. He heard it again and rode toward a deep gully. He looked over the edge. There he saw a shivering colt in the deep snow.

154

David climbed off his horse and jumped down beside the frightened colt. He tried to push it up the steep bank, but he couldn't move the colt.

David called his father. In another minute the rancher jumped down beside him. He looked the colt over carefully.

"He's OK," David's father said after a few moments. "Just had a bad fall. If he's been trapped here in the deep snow for very long, he must be hungry."

David watched his father talk to the frightened colt until it was quiet. Then he gently helped the little animal climb up and over the steep edge of the gully.

"He's a strong little fellow," said the rancher. "Has a lot of spirit too. This star marking on his nose is a good sign."

His father held the colt while David rubbed snow from its shivering sides and legs. The colt whinnied softly, as if to say thank you, and then kicked up his heels as he ran off toward the other colts.

"Wait!" called David, watching him gallop around the cliff. "Oh, Dad . . . he's gone."

David felt his father's hand on his shoulder. "Something tells me that is the colt you want," said the rancher.

"He's the one," cried David. "Can we catch him?"

"We can try," replied his father.

156

They got on their horses and rode through the herd, looking for the colt. They rode for a long time, while the wind grew colder and snowflakes blew more thickly all around them.

"Well, there are others," said David's father after a while. He lassoed a frisky young horse and pulled it toward them. "How about this one?" he asked. "He's lively enough for a boy like you."

David shook his head. "Dad, you said I could have any colt I choose for my birthday. . . ."

"That's right, son."

"I—I want the other colt."

"OK, David," said his father. "If you have your heart set on him, we'll find him for you."

The rancher set free the colt at the end of his rope. Then he led the way back into the gullies.

It was snowing harder now, and large, fat flakes hid the sky. After a while David's father said, "I'm afraid this is going to be a bad storm. We'd better head for the ranch house before we get lost. We'll look for your colt another time."

David nodded. He had heard about men getting lost in storms like this and losing their lives. He rode beside his father, as they tried to keep to the trail.

157

Suddenly David heard a whinny. Looking through the thick curtain of snow, he saw the young colt they had tried so hard to find.

"Look, Dad," he cried. "It's my colt!"

The colt stood still as David and his father rode toward him. Then suddenly he dashed away and a few moments later dashed back again.

"I think he's trying to tell us something," David shouted above the roar of the storm. "He acts as if he's trying to lead us somewhere."

"I think you're right," agreed his father. "Let's follow him and see."

The colt disappeared behind a cliff. David and his father followed. As they came closer, they found the colt standing in a large cave.

"Golly!" gasped David.

"I didn't know there was a cave in this part of the range," said his father. "We can wait here until the storm is over. You surely picked a smart colt, son."

They rode into the cave and got off their horses. As soon as David's feet touched the ground, the colt trotted happily over to him.

"Looks as if he likes you, son," said David's father. "Have you picked a name for him yet?"

David grinned. "I think I'll call him Snowdrift because that's where I found him."

The rancher laughed. "That's a good name for him." He patted the colt. "Yes, sir, he's a mighty fine colt."

After the storm passed, David and his father started back to the ranch. "Just to be on the safe side, we'll put a rope on this young fellow," said David's father.

Snowdrift didn't seem to mind. He trotted merrily along behind his young master as they headed back to the ranch. David had a big grin on his face. This was truly a happy birthday.

LESLIE F. HARCUS

159

Frontier Day

Have there been times when you could hardly wait for tomorrow to come?

The children at St. Michael's School felt that way. They were counting the hours until the rodeo would start on the next morning. There would be races, trick riding, roping, and Indian dances.

From the windows of the school the children could see cowboys and cowgirls who had come to town for the rodeo.

160

The town was gay, with bands playing and flags flying. The best part of all to the children at St. Michael's was that school would be closed on the opening day of the rodeo.

Now they could all go to the rodeo to see Joan in the pony race. The boys and girls had chosen Joan, who lived at Rising Sun Ranch, to race for St. Michael's. Joan was not as big as some of the other girls, but she was the best rider of all.

On the morning of the rodeo Joan was up early. She put on her cowgirl riding clothes and reached for her high-heeled boots. Then she started to walk toward the barn where her pony Bright Eyes was waiting.

161

Her mother saw her. "Come back and eat your breakfast," she called.

Joan was so excited she hardly knew what she ate.

Her father patted Joan on the back. "I'll put Bright Eyes in the trailer. You and Mother and I will ride on the front seat of the truck."

When they reached the main street of the town, Joan saw the boys and girls from St. Michael's. They were crowded along the sidewalk, shouting, "Good luck, Joan! Ride fast."

162

The Frontier Day parade started. First came the band, playing a gay march. Then came cowboys and cowgirls, riding beautiful horses that stepped in time to the music. Indians tramped by to the beat of tom-toms. Last of all came the girls who were to be in the pony race. Joan was the very last one in line.

As she rode by the cheering crowd, Joan sat tightly in the saddle, too frightened even to smile. "Will I come in last?" she wondered.

The parade ended at the rodeo grounds, and the contests began. First came a race in which cowboys changed their saddles every few minutes as they jumped off and on the galloping horses.

The wild horse race came next.

Then came an Indian hoop dance. A little lad, called White Owl, played his flute while Indians picked up great white hoops, swung them over their heads and around their feet while they kept time to the music.

164

It was early afternoon before the Pony Race for girls began. Ponies of many colors were waiting to be saddled. Some of the ponies were black, some were fat brown ponies, and there was one spotted pony.

Bright Eyes, Joan's pony, was black and white. He stood quietly while Joan's father helped her get ready for the race.

Then the band began to play loud, gay music. Bright Eyes had never before heard band music. At the sound of the drums and horns, Bright Eyes began to dance. He swung to the left, then to the right. His feet seemed to be keeping time to the music.

Joan had trouble getting into the saddle. She dug her knees into the pony's sides and pushed the toes of her high-heeled boots into the stirrups.

"This is a race, Bright Eyes," she said. "This isn't a dance contest."

Bright Eyes kept on dancing.

Then came a signal from the judges' stand. The ponies and their riders were off! Down the track they rode, swinging around the corners, flashing past the grandstand.

Bright Eyes was running slowly. "We'll never win," Joan said to herself.

As if by signal, the band began to play again. The music was all Bright Eyes needed.

Prancing, dancing, the pony raced down the track. Round and round, they raced.

"I'll be in the hospital if you go any faster," whispered Joan.

From the corner of her eye, she saw that the other riders were now behind her. "We're winning, Bright Eyes!" she shouted. "Good boy!"

The band stopped playing as Joan and Bright Eyes, winners of the race, came to a stop at the judges' stand. The judges were smiling, and Joan could hear the cheers of the boys and girls from St. Michael's.

The judges called Joan to the stand and handed her a beautiful leather jacket, first prize of the Pony Race.

As Joan left the stand, wearing the jacket, the boys and girls from St. Michael's rushed toward her.

"We're so proud of you," they told her.

Joan laughed. "Bright Eyes should have the prize. He never ran so fast in all of his life."

Three Young Warriors

Tommy and Mark came to Camp St. Charles on the same summer day. The camp, run by Brothers of Mary, is in one of the green valleys of the Far West where Indians once lived.

"Brother, will you let Mark and me camp in the same tent?" Tommy asked Brother Andrew.

"I'll put the two of you in the same tent," said Brother Andrew, "and Francis will be there, too."

Tommy and Mark did not know Francis, but they soon found that he was a very quiet boy. He did not talk to them about his school or his family or his friends.

"Maybe he hasn't any friends," said Tommy.

"That's his bad luck," said Mark.

The first night, as the boys sat around a campfire, Brother Andrew told them about the Indians who once lived in this valley.

"Sometimes," explained the Brother, "they did not have enough meat to feed their families. Then they would break camp and travel to another place with the hope of finding buffaloes."

"Buffaloes!" shouted the boys. "Did the Indians catch them?"

"Yes," replied Brother Andrew, "they were brave hunters. Sometimes the Indians would see a great herd of buffaloes moving across the plains. Clouds of dust rose as the buffaloes cut deep trails into the earth."

Just then Francis asked a question. "Could you tell us this story, Brother, in the Indian sign language?"

Brother Andrew laughed and lifted a stick from the ground. "I'll tell you the end of the story," he said. Then he made some pictures in the soft earth.

"Can you read it, Francis?" asked Brother Andrew.

"I'd like to try," said Francis.   He began slowly, "In the morning warrior kill.   At night much food in Indian camp."

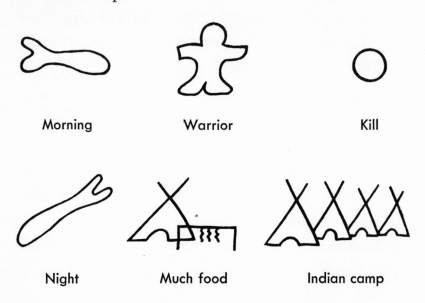

Morning   Warrior   Kill

Night   Much food   Indian camp

Mark sniffed.   "Mr. Know-It-All!" he whispered to Tommy.

But Tommy was thinking of something else.   "Let's play we're Indian warriors while we're here at camp. I'll be Silver Bow."

"You can call me Little Bear," said Mark.

Francis heard them, but he said nothing.

170

The next morning Brother Andrew told twelve of the boys that it was their turn to ride the camp horses up the side of the mountain. Tommy and Mark and Francis were among the twelve.

"We'll make believe we're hunting buffaloes, Silver Bow," Mark said to Tommy.

"We'll catch 'em, Little Bear," said Tommy.

Halfway up the side of the mountain Mark said in a low voice to Tommy, "Let's have a race. Just you and I, Silver Bow."

"My horse can beat yours, Little Bear," boasted Tommy.

"Hurry up," Mark scolded, "or Mr. Know-It-All will come too."

171

The two boys raced out ahead of the other riders. As they galloped along they saw something move across the trail just in front of them.

"Look! It's a rattlesnake!" shouted Tommy.

Mark, turning in his saddle, suddenly fell from his horse.

"Look out! Look out!" screamed Tommy. "The snake!"

The rattlesnake lay on the dusty trail before them. It had holes for a nose, and its tongue flashed out, red and quick, *s—s—s—s*.

"Don't move," shouted a voice behind them.

Looking over his shoulder, Tommy saw Francis riding toward them. The boys had not seen him leave the other riders and follow them down the trail.

"What can we do?" cried Tommy.

Francis slipped quickly from his saddle and picked up a sharp stone. He took careful aim, and then threw it at the rattlesnake. The danger was over!

173

Mark rose from the ground, his face white and his hands shaking. "You saved my life," he gasped. "How can I ever thank you, Francis?"

Francis smiled shyly. "That's all right," he said. "I'm glad I was here to help."

The three boys rode back down the trail to tell the other riders what had happened.

That night, as all the boys sat around the campfire, Tommy spoke to Brother Andrew. "You know what happened today, Brother?" he asked.

"I heard something about it," nodded Brother Andrew. "You and Mark were playing that you were Indian warriors. You should have stayed with the other boys. You were lucky that Francis came along."

"We surely were," agreed Tommy. "All this started with a game between Mark and me. He called himself Little Bear and I was Silver Bow. Now that Francis is our friend, we want to call him Snake Killer."

"You'll be friends now, I'm sure," smiled the Brother.

"We certainly will," Tommy said. "We want to put Indian signs on our tent that will show that we are three good friends. Will you help us?"

Again Brother Andrew took a stick and made signs in the soft ground. They looked like this:

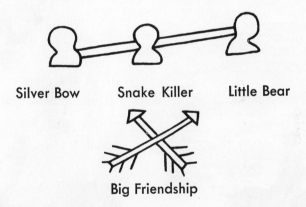

Silver Bow   Snake Killer   Little Bear

Big Friendship

The next morning the three boys painted the signs on their tent. It was the start of a long happy summer at Camp St. Charles, a summer the boys would never forget.

Young Cowboy

I'm up at dawn
　　Of every day,
I saddle my horse
　　And ride away.

In rain and sun,
　　Through ice and snow,
I mount my horse
　　And off I go!

In wind and dust,
　　Through sleet or hail,
I drive the cattle
　　Down the trail.

I'm on the go
　　From sun to sun
To get my chores
　　And work all done!

Day in, day out,
　　With little change,
I rope and brand
　　And ride the range!

NONA KEEN DUFFY

A Real Cowboy

Wander Is Lost

As Danny and Slim were riding the range near the mountains, Slim stopped and said, "Look at that herd of whitefaced cattle out in the sun!"

Danny pulled up beside him and turned to look across the range.

Some of the cattle were quietly eating grass. Others were resting. Several of the calves were playing, running in and out of the herd.

Slim and Danny rode through the herd to make sure they were all right.

"I don't see Wander and her twin calves," said Danny.

177

"I guess she has wandered off again," said Slim. "It's bad when any of the cattle wander too far from the herd. There are wolves in the mountains. When they find a cow or a calf alone, they may run after her and pull her down. A cow will fight for her calf, but she hasn't much chance against a wolf."

"I hope a wolf doesn't catch Wander and her twins," said Danny.

"They may be over near the trees," said Slim. "I'll ride this way to see. You ride that way. If I find them first, I'll call you."

"And if I find them first, I'll call you," said Danny.

Danny rode until he came to the fence. Then he came to a place where the fence had been broken, and the wire was down. There he thought he saw tracks of cattle that had walked across the wire.

"Get up, Ginger," he said, and the pony stepped over the wire.

Ahead of them there was a pool of water made by a spring. In the mud by the pool Danny saw tracks. He saw that a cow and two calves had stopped there.

"Come on, Ginger," he said. "Wander and her twins were here. We'll find them and drive them back."

178

Soon Danny came to a canyon with high cliffs on both sides. Wander's tracks turned into the canyon.

Thinking that he saw Wander ahead, Danny shouted, "Hey! Hey!" But it was only a rock.

He rode up the canyon until he came to two trails. He saw Wander's tracks on one of them and knew that was the one to take.

The trail ran up and down, between trees and over rocks. As he rode around every bend Danny looked for Wander.

At last Danny found the cow and her two calves under a tree. He started to drive them back, but Wander tried to run away. Ginger was a good cow pony and ran in front of her, driving her back.

"Now," said Danny, "back to the range you go."

Then he saw that it was getting dark. Night came early in the canyon because its high walls kept out the setting sun.

Danny tried to make the cow and calves go faster by shouting, "Hey! Hey! Move along! We have to get out of here!"

As it got darker, Danny had a hard time keeping on the trail.

"I never saw that tree before," he said when his leg bumped it as Ginger walked by. "I must be off the trail that leads out of the canyon."

He called, "Hi, Slim! Hi!"

There was no answer. Only his own voice came back. "Hi, Slim! Hi!"

Night

It was quite dark now, and Danny was worried. "What should I do?" he said to the cow pony. "I guess the best thing would be to camp here for the night and wait until morning to find the way out."

He tied the pony to a tree. Then he took a rope, put it around Wander's head, as he had seen Slim do, and tied her to another tree.

"That's to keep you from wandering off again, Wander," he said as he started to gather some dry wood for a fire.

After the fire was made, Danny lay down on the pine needles and tried to sleep, but there were strange sounds in the night.

There was a soft sound like someone whispering. That was the wind in the pine trees. A long way off an animal was howling. Danny didn't know what it was.

Ginger was not asleep. Wander was not asleep. The calves were close to her. They all seemed to be afraid.

Danny put more wood on the fire. When the sparks flew up, he saw something move out in the night. It looked like a big gray dog, and it moved without a sound. It was a wolf.

Danny picked up a rock and threw it as hard as he could.

For a long time the wolf didn't come back. Then Danny saw it again. He saw its shiny yellow eyes.

Danny threw all the rocks he could find, but the wolf kept coming back, its yellow eyes shining in the dark.

When Danny had no more rocks to throw, he shouted to drive the wolf back. That kept the wolf away for a while.

Then it was back again, no longer afraid of the shouts, and it came closer.

Danny had a new idea. He took a burning stick out of the fire and threw it. The wolf howled and ran.

All night Danny kept the fire burning so that he could throw burning sticks at the wolf when it came back.

At last daylight began to come over the canyon walls, and Danny did not have to worry about the wolf. It had gone far back into the canyon.

He was so tired he could hardly move, but he started to put out the fire.

Suddenly Ginger's ears stood up.

"What's the matter?" asked Danny.

He listened. Something was moving in the canyon not far away.

Someone shouted, "Danny! Danny!"

Danny forgot he was sleepy and tired. He turned and ran down the canyon trail and just around the bend he met Slim!

"Danny! Where have you been? I looked for you all night," said Slim. "When the sun came up, I tracked you into this canyon."

"I found Wander and the calves," said Danny, "but it got dark before I could find my way out of the canyon."

"What's this?" asked Slim. "Look at these wolf tracks!"

"Yes," said Danny. "A wolf tried to get Wander and the calves. I threw rocks and burning sticks to keep it away."

"And you stayed here all night and kept the hungry wolf away?" said Slim. "Danny, this makes you a real cowboy. Taking care of his cattle is the cowboy's most important job. Last night you took care of your cattle, and no cowboy could have done better."

"And that's what I've always wanted to be—a real cowboy," said Danny.

CLYDE ROBERT BULLA

Golden Days

Thanksgiving Hymn

For flowers that bloom about our feet,
For tender grass, so fresh, so sweet,
For song of bird and hum of bee,
For all things fair we hear or see—
      Father in Heaven, we thank Thee!

For blue of stream and blue of sky,
For pleasant shade of branches high,
For fragrant air and cooling breeze,
For beauty of the blooming trees—
      Father in Heaven, we thank Thee!

For mother-love and father-care,
For brothers strong and sisters fair,
For love at home and here each day,
For guidance, lest we go astray,
      Father in Heaven, we thank Thee!

For this new morning with its light,
For rest and shelter of the night,
For health and food, for love and friends,
For everything His goodness sends,
      Father in Heaven, we thank Thee!

AUTHOR UNKNOWN

Shake-the-Basket Day

The New Friend

Friendship is a lovely thing.

Molly is an American girl, who lives in a village near an American Air Base in Holland where her father is a jet pilot.

She goes to the American Air Base school where she is taught many of the same things you are learning here in America.

Each morning, five days a week, she rides to school with other American children in the school bus. On Sunday, when Molly goes to Holy Mass at St. Martin's Church in the village, she kneels and prays with many Dutch boys and girls.

One Sunday a little Dutch girl waited outside the church and spoke to Molly.

"My name is Katrina," she said.

Molly was surprised to hear this Dutch girl speaking English.

"I wish I could tell you my name in Dutch," Molly replied, "but I'm afraid I'll never learn to speak Dutch."

188

"I wish I could speak more English," said Katrina.
"If we played together, I could learn more English,
and you would soon speak Dutch."

Together they walked back through the village
from the church. "Come to my house and meet the
rest of my family," invited Molly.

That was the beginning of many happy visits
between the two little girls.

When Molly went to Katrina's house, she met Jan and Hilda, Katrina's older brother and sister. They could speak a little English, and so the four children played games and sang songs, sometimes in English and sometimes in Dutch. Before long, Molly was learning to speak Dutch very well.

One day, early in November, Molly went to visit her friends. They were talking excitedly about their plans for a very special feast day.

"What day is that?" asked Molly.

"Didn't you ever hear of Shake–the–Basket Day?" asked Katrina in surprise.

Molly shook her head. She had no idea what Shake–the–Basket Day meant.

"It's St. Martin's Day," explained Hilda. "He is the saint for whom our church is named."

"Oh, I know about St. Martin," said Molly. "He was the saint who cut his cloak in half and gave part of it to a beggar to keep him warm."

"In Holland we never forget St. Martin's kindness," Hilda went on. "We fill baskets with food and carry them to the poor orphans of the village every year on his feast day."

"Why do you call it Shake–the–Basket Day?" asked Molly. "Do you shake baskets filled with food?"

Katrina laughed. "No, we cook the food at home. Then we carry corn and nuts in big bags, and we all have fun shaking them in wire baskets over a campfire. That is why we call it Shake–the–Basket Day."

"I wish I could help the orphans, too," said Molly eagerly.

"Come with us to the Orphans' Home on St. Martin's Day," invited Katrina.

St. Martin's Feast Day

After Mass on November 11, which is the feast day of the good saint, the two girls walked back to Katrina's house.

Katrina's mother and the two older children were busy at work in the kitchen. Molly sniffed at the delicious smells which filled the room.

"What can I do?" she asked.

"Come and help me with the cooking," said the Dutch children's mother. "Katrina and Hilda and Jan will be put to work, too."

"I'm a good cook," said Hilda.

"Then stuff the goose," said her mother.

"I'll make the cookies," offered Katrina.

"How can I help?" asked Molly again.

Jan laughed. "You can put the pink frosting on the gingerbread," he said.

"Jan is lazy," said his mother, but she smiled and she told him to go out to the yard and carry a pile of wood to a gayly painted sleigh that was standing in front of the door.

For years and years, if there was snow on St. Martin's Day, the people of the village had gone in this sleigh to take food to the orphans. They did not ride bicycles or drive cars or even walk to the Orphans' Home. They always went in the sleigh pulled by two strong horses.

"We always go to the orphan's picnic on St. Martin's Day dressed as our grandparents once dressed years ago," said Hilda.

So Katrina rushed into her mother's room and, opening an old painted trunk, brought out three gay dresses that had been worn long, long ago.

"How beautiful!" exclaimed Molly. "May I wear one of them?"

"Of course you can wear one," Katrina's mother replied. She helped Molly put on the long, full skirt, the bright blouse, and the white cap.

Jan came out of his own room, dressed in the full trousers and the colorful shirt that had been worn by his grandfather. Then, stamping his feet, he began to sing. The noise, not only of the song but of the sound of his boots, filled the room, for Jan was wearing old wooden shoes that the Dutch call *klompen*.

"The orphans will be dressed in old Dutch costumes and wooden shoes, too," Hilda told Molly. "We see them every year."

When the goose was roasted and the cookies were cool and the gingerbread was covered with pink frosting, there came a knock on the heavy wooden front door.

Katrina and Jan raced through the rooms. "It's the Brother," announced Katrina excitedly.

"A brother?" asked Molly in surprise.

Hilda smiled. "He is one of the Christian Brothers from the Orphans' Home," she explained. "He has come to lead the way, for this is how we go every St. Martin's Day."

Again there came a knock on the door.

"Open the door quickly, children," Katrina's mother called.

As the four children pulled with all their might at the heavy door, they played this old Dutch game.

KATRINA: Who's at the door there?

Who's at the door?

HILDA: See what he wants, Jan.

See what he wants.

JAN: What do you want, Brother?

What do you want?

BROTHER: Food for the poor children,

Food for the little ones.

The children opened the door and welcomed their good friend, Brother John Mark.

The Dutch children's father came in from the bright sleigh. "Ready to go?" he asked.

"Ready!" shouted the children, and Molly shouted the loudest, for she could now say it in Dutch.

Down the long village street the Brother and gift-givers of the village rode in the big red sleigh until they came to the mission. Jan and other boys of the village lifted out the firewood and the baskets of food.

Orphans rushed out to meet them. "Welcome! Welcome!" they shouted, and then, turning to Brother John Mark, they said, "Thank you!"

"Don't thank me," laughed the Brother. "Thank your good friends and thank the blessed St. Martin."

Then Brother asked God's blessing on the many gifts as he stood at the head of a long wooden table. All the delicious food brought by the people of the village was eaten—roast goose and pork and cheese and cookies and gingerbread. It was a wonderful feast.

Then the orphans built a campfire and, as the villagers handed them the long-handled wire baskets, the orphans toasted the corn and nuts.

"Shake–the–Basket!" they all shouted, until the corn was popped white and the nuts were a golden brown.

As a jet roared high in the sky, they all looked up.

"That could be my daddy's plane," Molly cried. "He's flying today to show you that all of us at the American Air Base are your friends."

"We shall always be friends," said Brother John Mark. "May God bless America, and may God bless Holland."

Friendship is a lovely thing.

197

A Carol

Mary had a Baby,
Jesus was His Name.
On a winter's evening
Quietly He came.

No great lords received Him
Or answered at His call.
His Crown was Light Triumphant,
His Kingdom was a stall.

His servants were the oxen
Who knelt the manger by
Lowing, "Holy! Holy!
Thou Son of God Most High."

Never was there Mother
As sweet or good or mild,
And never was there Infant
Like that Holy Child.

IVY O. EASTWICK

Long, Long Ago

Winds through the olive trees
Softly did blow,
Round little Bethlehem
Long, long ago.

Sheep on the hillside lay
Whiter than snow;
Shepherds were watching them,
Long, long ago.

Then from the happy sky,
Angels bent low,
Singing their songs of joy,
Long, long ago.

For in a manger bed,
Cradled we know,
Christ came to Bethlehem
Long, long ago.

AUTHOR UNKNOWN

A Knock at the Door

Once upon a time, many years ago, a young child was alone in a great city. It was Christmas Eve. The lighted streets were filled with people hurrying home, but no one stopped to speak to the ragged child with the longing eyes.

"Surely," he said to himself, "where there is so much joy there must be a little for me. Perhaps in this great house there will be room for a tired boy," and he knocked gently at the door.

The rooms inside were gay with candles and flowers. They were as light as if it were day. At one end of the hall stood a tall Christmas tree, loaded with presents. Around it children were singing and dancing.

The door opened, and a man with a cross voice spoke to the little lad.

"This is no place for you," he said. "Don't you know that this is Christmas Eve? If I see you here again, I shall call the master."

The child turned sadly from the door. Now the streets were almost empty, and the lamps began to go out.

The night grew colder, and snowflakes began to fall. In all the wide world this poor child seemed to be the only one without a home. He walked on into the poorer part of the city.

In the window of a neat cottage, a girl stood looking out at the falling snow. The boy could see the supper upon the table, the smiling mother, the happy children. A sudden hope made his heart leap, but when he opened the cottage gate, the girl frowned at him and turned away.

Over and over again the boy tried to find a welcome. Sometimes the maids were too busy to come to the door. Sometimes (and this was usually in one of the smaller houses) a tired mother would shake her head sadly and say, "I'm sorry, but my rooms are full tonight. You see, it is Christmas Eve."

Nowhere in all that great city did there seem to be room for one little boy. As it grew darker, the curtains were drawn over the windows, hiding the happy families as they made ready for the feast day. Then the streets seemed cold and lonely indeed.

At last the child came to the very poorest part of the city. And here, at the end of an ugly little street, he found a hut with one small window. There was no curtain, and from the light of a tiny Christmas candle, which had been set in the window, he could see into the room. By the fire sat a mother telling her children a story.

The child knocked softly at the door.

"Someone must be at the door," said the mother to her daughter. "Run quickly and open it. It is too stormy a night to keep anyone waiting, and, besides, it is Christmas Eve."

The girl ran to the door and threw it wide open. When the mother saw the shivering child on the step, she came forward and led him into the warm room.

"Oh, how cold you are!" she said, with a gentle arm about his shoulders. "And I am afraid that you are hungry too. Children, is the soup hot yet?"

"Oh, yes, mother," said her son, "and he must have every bit of it. I am sure I could eat it all myself—if I were hungry," he added quickly as his eyes met his mother's. "You know we had a good dinner and do not need it. And may he sleep in my bed? He is such a little boy. I can pile up some blankets on the floor for myself. Oh, Mother, do say that he may stay here tonight!"

"Of course he will stay," she said warmly. "Did not Our Lord tell us that when we do things for others, we do it for Him? Make him welcome, children, for the sake of the sweet Babe of Bethlehem."

Then the boy and girl went forward to take the child by the hand. But even as they smiled upon him, a heavenly light filled the tiny room. The house seemed to grow and grow until it reached the sky itself. From angel voices came the song, "Glory to God in the highest; and on earth peace to men of good will!"

The mother and her children fell to their knees, but the wonderful Child was no longer there.

"Was it the Christ Child?" the children asked. "And has He left us?"

"He will never leave you," said the mother, "so long as you truly love Him. Never again perhaps will this wonderful sight come to us, but we must love Him and serve Him always."

A LEGEND

Candlemas Day

In the City of Rome
On Candlemas Day
The Pope blesses candles
And gives them away,
Till all, high and low,
Before him have passed,
The Cardinals first
And the Sacristan last.
Then the candles are lighted
So golden and gay,
To the sound of sweet singing
On Candlemas Day.

ELEANOR FARJEON

The Light of the World

Far across the old gray city Carla heard the bells.

"Seven o'clock! Seven o'clock!" sang the big brass bell in the high stone tower of the city hall.

"Seven o'clock! Seven o'clock!" rang the shining silver bell in the tall clock in the palace of the king.

Then came the sweet sound of the four great golden bells of the cathedral. "Seven o'clock! Seven o'clock!" they called out over treetops and housetops.

"I'll be late," cried Carla.

She raced across the stone bridge over a wide blue river and up the little streets that led to a hill on the edge of the city.

It was Candlemas Day.

Carla's dress was thin, and the wind was cold. Her shoes were old, and the paving stones in the street were big and rough.

Carla did not care. She was on her way to the cathedral where the bishop and the priests, the king and the queen, and all the people would walk in procession on this day to honor the Holy Child and His Blessed Mother.

Carla knew the meaning of Candlemas Day. Her grandmother, who was too old to walk across the wide city, had told her. "Forty days after the Holy Child had been born at Bethlehem, His Blessed Mother carried Him for the first time into the temple at Jerusalem."

"She must have walked many miles," said Carla.

"She wanted to present the Child Jesus to the House of God," explained her grandmother.

"Why do we carry lighted candles?" asked Carla.

"To honor the Holy Child, who is the Light of the World," the old lady answered.

"Some day I shall see the beautiful procession in the cathedral," said Carla.

"When you are old enough to cross the city alone," promised her grandmother.

Now the day had come.

In the east the sun began to shine through dark winter clouds. Coaches rolled past Carla, and she could hear the drivers shouting, "Hurry! Hurry!" to the horses.

A golden coach, drawn by four white horses, came down the road. Drivers in red coats and footmen dressed in sky-blue jackets sat straight and tall on the open seats. Inside the coach Carla could see a beautiful lady, a tall man, and a little boy.

"The Queen! The King! The little Prince!" Carla ran beside the coach for a moment. Then it was gone.

Now no one but the little girl could be seen on the road. "They are all in church," Carla told herself, as she raced against the winter wind. An icy twig caught and tore her thin dress.

"No one will see it," she told herself, "for no one will notice a poor girl like me."

The cathedral was filled when Carla reached the top of the hill. Men, women, and children filled every corner.

In seats near the altar rail sat the king and the queen and the little prince. Everyone in the church was carrying a blessed candle.

"Am I too late?" she asked a woman standing near the door. "Will I be without a candle?"

"You are too late," said the woman. "The bishop blessed all the candles and gave them to us at the altar."

Carla's eyes were filled with tears as she knelt upon the stone floor beside the great door. Above her, a hundred voices began to sing. Their music filled the great cathedral, "A Light to the glory of Thy people."

Carla whispered the words: "A Light to the glory of Thy people."

Over the heads of the people she could see the bishop. "Let us set forth in peace," he said.

The people answered, "In the name of Christ, Amen," and lighted their candles.

The procession began. First came the priests and the altar boys, lighted candles in their hands. Behind them came the bishop, who carried a statue of the Holy Child. After him walked the king and the queen and the little prince, each carrying a shining candle. Then, in the gleam of candlelight, walked the men and women and children of the old gray city.

The hundred voices again sang praise to the Son of God: "Bless these candles, which Thy servants carry today."

The procession neared the wide door. Carla stepped out of the way.

The bishop noticed the little girl and stopped. "You have no candle," he said.

Carla bowed her head. "I was late," she whispered softly. "I walked many miles."

The procession stopped. "A candle for the child," said the bishop.

"A candle for the child," called out the priests.

"A candle for the child," shouted the people.

Then a boy stepped forward. "She may carry my candle," he said. It was the young prince.

The priests smiled, and the bishop smiled, and they moved through the doorway of the cathedral.

Then Carla heard the king say, "The child must walk with us."

The queen held out her hand. Her voice was sweet and gentle. "Come, my child."

The bishop, the priests, and the altar boys moved out into the sunlight, out toward the city square. Behind them, candles burning, walked the king, the queen, and the ragged little girl.

Carla looked at the prince. "Now he has no candle," she thought. "I should not have taken his blessed light."

The young prince smiled, but he did not speak. He was giving thanks to God because on this day he had brought such great joy to a poor little girl.

"Glory be to God," sang the faithful, rich and poor, young and old. Their voices rose in praise of the Holy Child, the Light of the World, who had said, "Love one another as I love you."

The sweet golden bells of the cathedral sang out the blessing of the Holy Child. They rang across the bridges and the wide blue river, and up and down the streets of the old gray city on that Candlemas Day.

KATHERINE RANKIN

Waking-up Time

Sally had never been up so early before in her life.
She shivered into her clothes in the gray light and
hurried to brush her hair. Her sister, Avis, was
ready and waiting for her.

Avis had gone to early Mass on Easter morning
many times, but Sally had never gone so early before,
and she was excited.

Just as she finished brushing her hair, the church bell began to ring.

How queer and gray the things outside looked without the sun's bright face! She took Avis' hand and walked quietly, feeling grown-up in her new white gloves.

"The earth is still asleep," said Avis.

"But the birds know it will soon be bright. Listen to them!" whispered Sally.

The church was lighted by candles and filled with the smell of spring flowers. It, too, seemed strange before sunrise.

Sally sat very still, listening to the story of the three women who came so early in the morning to Jesus' tomb. How sad it must have been to see the angel sitting by the empty tomb!

"He is risen!" cried the angel's happy voice. "He is risen!"

And then, thought Sally, the sun must have begun to shine, just as it was shining now in little golden ruffles on the treetops outside. And the birds, which had been only twittering before, must have burst into happy song, just as the great organ now burst into happy music.

The church bells began to ring again, and now they sounded full of joy. They said: "Come! Awake! Jesus is risen! Springtime is here again. Awake, sleepy world, awake!"

As soon as Sally got home she took off her new white gloves and went to the chicken yard to see if there were eggs for breakfast. Perhaps it was because she had taken off her gloves, but now she no longer wanted to walk quietly.

She felt so wide-awake and happy that she wanted to skip and hop and run. Out in the chicken yard there was a great clucking.

"What is the matter?" asked Sally. "Don't you know that this is Easter morning?"

The big rooster crowed. It seemed as if he were saying, "That's why we are happy! Spring is here! Winter is past, and the waking-up time has come again."

"Peep! Peep! Peep!" cried the baby chicks. For a long time they had slept in the dark little houses. But now they had broken their walls and come into the sunshine, and they were happy, too.

The brown hen clucked. Her babies had come out of their shells, and she was happy.

"Do you have any eggs for my breakfast?" asked Sally as she followed the little white hen into the chicken house and peeped into the nests. Every nest had a round white egg in it, and soon Sally's apron was full.

"Thank you! Thank you!" cried Sally gayly, "and happy Easter to you all!"

Sally had to walk very carefully with an apron full of eggs. But when she carried them all into the kitchen without cracking one, she was ready to skip outdoors again and pick some flowers for the table.

As she crossed the grass to the tulip bed Sally suddenly stopped and held her breath. There, at the edge of the grass, was a wild brown rabbit. He looked at Sally with round, gentle eyes.

"Oh," said Sally softly, "I thought you would be afraid."

The rabbit made no noisy sounds of joy such as the chickens did, but Sally knew by the way he twitched his whiskers and pointed his ears that he was happy, too.

He looked at her as much as to say, "It is waking-up time, and there are lovely green things to eat, and I am very happy and not afraid of anything!" With a frisk of his white tail, he turned and hopped away.

"Good-by, brown bunny. Happy Easter to you!" called Sally.

The tulips stood in pleasant rows, lifting their deep-red cups toward the blue sky.

"We are giving thanks, Sally," they seemed to say. "Lift your eyes to the blue sky and give thanks, too. It is waking-up time, and we are glad. Last fall we were round brown bulbs. We lay in the ground and slept. Snow covered us, and frost chilled us. We thought we should never wake up again. But now the spring sun and rain have given us new life. We have put on our brightest colors to show our joy that Christ has risen."

Sally picked three of the brightest tulips for the breakfast table. The sun streamed in across the white tablecloth and shone on Sally's blue egg cup with the round white egg in it. Sally looked up at the blue sky and saw a happy bird fly across it, singing.

"All the world seems to know that Jesus is risen," she said. Then she bowed her head and said, "Dear Lord, we thank You for waking-up time. Amen."

CAROL RYRIE BRINK

Easter

Spring bursts today,
For Christ is risen and all earth's at play.

Flash forth, thou sun.
The rain is over and gone, its work is done.

Winter is past,
Sweet spring is come at last, is come at last.

Break forth this morn
In roses, thou but yesterday a thorn.

Uplift thy head,
O pure white lily, through the winter dead.

Sing, creatures, sing,
Angels and men and birds and everything!

CHRISTINA ROSSETTI

220

Easter Morning

Pines whose whispers fill the air . . .
Birches bowed as if in prayer . . .
Benedictions everywhere
    On Easter morning.

On the mountain's azure crest,
Far above the placid breast
Of the lake, are clouds at rest
    On Easter morning.

Butterflies, and birds, and bees . . .
Altar-hills, and singing trees . . .
Faith is born of things like these
    On Easter morning.

LOUISE ABNEY

221

To the Teacher

The Story Tree is a transitional book, designed to provide a plateau period of growth during which skills already taught during the primary program are more completely assimilated. This assimilation of basic skills is implemented through the use of stories of high interest appeal, stimulating to the child's imagination, and which can be read between the third- and fourth-grade levels.

In order that pupils may have an opportunity to apply the techniques of independent word-recognition developed in the word-study program of the primary grades, only a limited vocabulary control has been instituted. A full explanation of the method used is given in the introduction to the *Manual for Teaching The Story Tree*. The following 117 words, of which 26 are sight words and 91 of which can be independently attacked by the pupils, are considered as unfamiliar at this level and are so treated in the manual lesson plans.

WORD LIST

Unit I
8. . . .
9. (*Poem*)

10. bumbershoot
11. *whuff*
12. . . .
13. . . .
14. . . .
15. pilot
16. . . .
17. *swish*

18. Azor
    Matthew
19. . . .

20. root beer
21. . . .
22. blinked
    plop
23. gunky
24. . . .
25. . . .

26. (*Poem*)

27. . . .
28. disturb
29. rude
30. . . .
31. . . .
32. . . .

33. taxicab
    granny
34. . . .
35. . . .
36. among
37. . . .

Unit II
38. . . .
39. (*Poem*)

40. Ludi
    St. Bernard
    Lodge
    monks

41. panting
42. shrine
    faded
43. . . .
44. moaning
45. nip
46. . . .
47. . . .

48. Totaram
49. jungle
50. . . .
51. . . .
52. . . .
53. . . .

222

223

ABCDEFGHIJ 06987654
PRINTED IN THE UNITED STATES OF AMERICA